The Hippocratic
Ancient Lessons for the

John Fabre

The ROYAL
SOCIETY of
MEDICINE
PRESS Limited

ACKNOWLEDGEMENTS

The author would like to thank the Publishers and the Loeb Classical Library for permission to reprint extracts from HIPPOCRATES: VOLUMES I–VIII, translated by WHS Jones, ET Withington and P Potter, Cambridge, Mass: Harvard University Press, 1923–1995, and also the Wellcome Institute Library, London for permission to reproduce the illustrations

For my parents

ISBN 1-85315-339-7

Design by Spot On Design, Leighton Buzzard, Bedfordshire
Phototypeset by Dobbie Typesetting Limited, Tavistock, Devon
Printed in Great Britain by Ebenezer Baylis, The Trinity Press, Worcester

Contents

Foreword

The genesis of this booklet was a lecture given at the 8th Walter Brendel Symposium on Applied Immunology and Microcirculation in February 1997, at Axams in Austria. Professor Brendel, then Director of the Institute for Surgical Research in Munich, organized the first of these annual 3 day meetings in Kitzbühel in 1969. The more recent meetings in Axams have been named in his honour, following his death in 1989. At each meeting, someone gives a 'Relaxing from Immunology Lecture' at the end of the second day's scientific lectures.

Following a suggestion (from me) for a talk on Hippocratic medicine, the current Director of the Institute, Professor Konrad Messmer, promptly invited me to address the issue. I soon discovered that reading for pleasure is one thing, but reading for a lecture is quite another. Over a period of several months, virtually all of my spare time was given to re-reading the Hippocratic treatises I had read, and reading afresh those I had planned to read over a year or two. Going through the greater part of the Hippocratic Corpus in a short time, and taking notes on points of relevance or interest to the current day, was a most interesting and probably fairly unique experience. The prospect of addressing my colleagues on this subject provided the potent spur needed for this major exercise.

Rather than let this experience dissipate with time, I have put together those parts of the Corpus which might interest a modern general reader, especially someone training in, or practising, medicine, or one of the allied health professions. However, relatively little medical jargon has been used, and I have included a glossary of medical terms for the non-medical reader. The basic objective is to give an idea of the life and times of a Hippocratic doctor, as revealed by the ancient writings of the Corpus, especially when they might be of value or interest to our own times.

I hope you enjoy the book.

Professor J Fabre
November 1997

Foreword

Chapter 1

Introduction

Everyone knows that Hippocrates was a famous doctor of ancient times, and that modern medicine is in some way connected with him. However, from my experience, hardly anyone has any knowledge of Hippocrates himself or of that great body of ancient medical writings known as the Hippocratic Corpus. This is in spite of the fact that the Hippocratic Corpus formed the basis of Western medical practice for over 2,000 years, almost into our own times.

The Corpus contains some of the most ancient extant Greek medical writings. To read these writings is to communicate directly, by the magic of the written word, with doctors who lived and practised around 2,500 years ago, in a setting utterly different to that in which we live today. The problem, however, is that the Corpus is not easy to read, even with the beautiful translations of the Loeb Classical Library series[1-8]. It can be obscure, repetitive, apparently irrelevant and, perhaps of most importance, it is not set out as a logical and systematic exposition of ancient medicine. One cannot refer to a particular chapter in a particular treatise to learn about the Hippocratic doctors' view on any particular point. Having personally read the greater part of the Corpus, I think it is fair to say that it is only by reading the whole that one can come away with a clear impression of Hippocratic thinking on particular issues.

Many people potentially interested in Hippocratic medicine will have neither the time nor the inclination to read through the Corpus in its entirety. What I have done, therefore, is to extract relevant pieces from many disparate treatises of the Corpus and then group them under eight main headings. In this way, by providing a systematic structure lacking in the original, I hope to make the ideas and sentiments of the Corpus far more accessible. Most importantly, by quoting the ancient texts directly, I think that we can come very close to the minds and thoughts of the Hippocratic doctors. We can see and hear precisely how they themselves articulated their views on many issues important to them, which are just as important and interesting for us today. Letting the Hippocratic doctors speak directly to us is, I am sure, the best way for a reader to gain access to the medical world of ancient Greece. The eight headings I have chosen are:

1. The Hippocratic doctor: personality, ethics, environment
2. The Hippocratic tradition of rational medicine

3. Hippocratic ideas of health and disease
4. Interesting case histories and disease descriptions
5. Hippocratic approaches to therapy
6. The treatment of fractures, dislocations and other injuries
7. Interesting miscellaneous points
8. Ancient clinical genetics

The major basis of my studies has been the Loeb series on Hippocrates. The Loeb Classical Library aims to translate into English all significant Greek and Latin texts, a task begun in the early part of this century, and still continuing. In the case of the Hippocratic Corpus, Volumes I to IV were first published between 1923 and 1931, and Volumes V to VIII from 1988 to 1995[1-8]. This covers the greater part of the Corpus, but two more volumes are due, probably in late 1998 or 1999.

TABLE 1. The Hippocratic treatises covered in this volume*

Affections	Law
Airs, Waters, Places	Nature of Man
Ancient Medicine	Nutriment
Aphorisms	On Fractures
Breaths	On Generation
Decorum	On Joints
Dentition	On Wounds in the Head
Diseases I	Physician
Diseases II	Places in Man
Diseases III	Precepts
Epidemics I	Prognostic
Epidemics II	Prorrhetic I
Epidemics III	Prorrhetic II
Epidemics IV	Regimen I
Epidemics V	Regimen II
Epidemics VI	Regimen III
Epidemics VII	Regimen IV (Dreams)
Fistulas	Regimen in Acute Diseases
Fleshes	Regimen in Acute Diseases (Appendix)
Glands	Regimen in Health
Haemorrhoids	The Art
Humours	The Oath
Instruments of Reduction	The Sacred Disease
Internal Affections	Ulcers
In the Surgery	Use of Liquids

*All from the Loeb Series[1-8] except On Generation[9].

The Hippocratic treatise On Generation (i.e. reproduction) has yet to be translated in the Loeb series, but has been translated into English in a Penguin Classic[9]. The treatises I have covered, namely all of those in Vol. I–VIII of the Loeb series, together with On Generation, are listed in Table 1. There are some interesting references in these treatises to the transmission of parental characteristics to children. However, to give a better idea of ancient concepts of genetics, I have drawn also on the massive work of Aristotle in this area[10].

These are my own personal gleanings from a great mass of writing. My intention is to illuminate the life and times of the Hippocratic doctor, perhaps sometimes to inspire us with their principles and their ingenuity, and occasionally to amuse us.

Chapter 2

Essential background to the Hippocratic corpus

Hippocrates was born around 460 BC or 450 BC on the island of Cos in the eastern Aegean, very close to what is now Turkey but which in classical times was the Greek colony of Ionia (Figure 1). Few details of his life are known, but his fame as a physician is well documented, as is the fact that he taught medicine. He died around 370 BC. Interestingly enough, that other great medical figure of ancient times, Galen, also a Greek, was born some 500 years later (129 AD) close by in Pergamum.

The Hippocratic Corpus comprises some 60 or so treatises, among which are the earliest extant Greek medical writings. They were actually written by many authors, mainly over the period 420 BC–350 BC. None of the treatises can be attributed with certainty to any particular author, but it is probable that Hippocrates wrote some of them. It is interesting to note that the treatises were written in the Ionian dialect, suggesting that the authors were all from Cos or the nearby regions. The style varies considerably from a series of short, concise points (e.g. Aphorisms) to longer discussions of individual conditions (e.g. Internal Affections) to case histories (e.g. Epidemics I).

The treatises comprising the Corpus were collated around 280 BC (some 100 years after the death of Hippocrates) in Alexandria in Egypt, apparently with the objective of forming a library for the education of medical students and doctors. Their attribution to Hippocrates would have given them a special status in the medical community. They have, since then, been translated into many languages and copied countless times, with some fragmentation and merging of treatises in the process[11].

By way of background, it is also worth noting the dates of Aristotle (384–322 BC). The later Hippocratic treatises would have been written while he was making his contributions to experimental biology (as well as philosophy). If Hippocrates can be described as the great clinician or clinician scientist of Classical Greece, there is no doubt that Aristotle is the great basic biologist of that time. His work on experimental biology (e.g. his ideas on reproduction and inheritance[10]) were of great relevance to medicine.

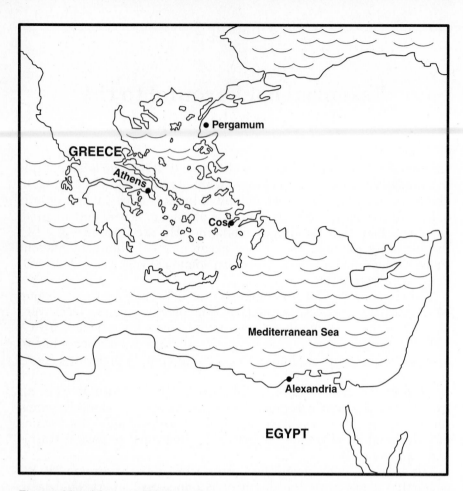

Figure 1. Map of the eastern Mediterranean.

Chapter 3

The Hippocratic doctor

A reading of the treatises can give a good idea of some aspects of the environment in which the Hippocratic doctors practised. Moreover, in a few treatises, the personality of the author comes through very strongly. Most interestingly, several treatises (Decorum, Precepts, Physician, and of course The Oath) are devoted to defining how doctors should behave.

I would like to begin, however, with a lovely description of medicine and what it is to be a doctor:

BREATHS, Ch. I: *"There are some arts which to those that possess them are painful, but to those that use them are helpful, a common good to laymen, but to those that practise them grievous. Of such arts there is one which the Greeks call medicine. For the medical man sees terrible sights, touches unpleasant things, and the misfortunes of others bring a harvest of sorrows that are peculiarly his; but the sick by means of the art rid themselves of the worst of evils, disease, suffering, pain and death"* (Loeb, Vol. II, p227).

By way of introduction, too, I would like to illustrate how difficult it is to divorce oneself from the present and to view things through the eyes of an ancient doctor. However much one tries, there nevertheless are many occasions while reading the Corpus when something will suddenly strike out from the pages and surprise. Here is the piece that caused me the greatest astonishment. It concerns the treatment of tonsillitis:

DISEASES II, Ch. 30: *"If tonsillitis occurs, there are swellings beneath the jaws on both sides which, if felt from the outside, are hard, and the whole uvula swells up. When the case is such, put a finger down the throat, and tear away the tonsils"* (Loeb, Vol. V, p245).

This casual, one-sentence description of a 'finger tonsillectomy', set among otherwise innocuous text, puts day-case surgery into perspective!

The preferred personality

The author of On Joints and On Fractures (possibly Hippocrates) was clearly someone of immense clinical experience, who wrote with great authority, and who was utterly disdainful of ostentation in clinical practice. Presumably he would have tried to instil these characteristics into his students, by example if nothing else. Consider these pieces:

ON FRACTURES, Ch. I: *"In fact the treatment of a fractured arm is not difficult, and is almost any practitioner's job, but I have to write a good deal about it because I know practitioners who have got credit for wisdom by putting arms in positions which ought rather to have given them a name for ignorance. And many other parts of this art are judged thus: for they praise what seems outlandish before they know whether it is good, rather than the customary which they already know to be good; the bizarre rather than the obvious"* (Loeb, Vol. III, p95).

ON JOINTS, Ch. LXXVII: *"What you should put first in all the practice of our art is how to make the patient well; and if he can be made well in many ways, one should choose the least troublesome. This is more honourable and more in accord with the art for anyone who is not covetous of the false coin of popular advertisement"* (Loeb, Vol. III, p383).

With regard to general demeanour, some very specific advice indeed is given, and I wonder how today's students would react to advice such as this from their teachers (!):

PHYSICIAN, Ch. 1: *"The dignity of a physician requires that he should look healthy, and as plump as nature intended him to be; for the common crowd consider those who are not of this excellent bodily condition to be unable to take care of others. Then he must be clean in person, well dressed, and anointed with sweet-smelling unguents that are beyond suspicion. For all these things are pleasing to people who are ill, and he must pay attention to this. In matters of the mind, let him be prudent, not only with regard to silence, but also in having a great regularity of life, since this is very important in respect of reputation; he must be a gentleman in character, and being this he must be grave and kind to all. For an over-forward obtrusiveness is despised, even though it may be very useful ... In appearance, let him be of a serious but not harsh countenance; for harshness is taken to mean arrogance and unkindness, while a man of controlled laughter and excessive gaiety is considered vulgar, and vulgarity especially must be avoided"* (Loeb, Vol. VIII, pp301,303).

DECORUM, Ch. VII: *"As all I have said is true, the physician must have at his command a certain ready wit, as dourness is repulsive both to the healthy and to the sick. He must also keep a most careful watch over himself, and neither expose much of his person nor gossip to laymen, but say only what is absolutely necessary"* (Loeb, Vol. II, p291).

DECORUM, Ch. XII: *"On entering bear in mind your manner of sitting, reserve, arrangement of dress, decisive utterance, brevity of speech, composure, bedside manners, care, replies to objections, calm self-control to meet the troubles that occur, rebuke of disturbance, readiness to do what has to be done"* (Loeb, Vol. II, p295).

There is a particularly charming piece indicating that doctors should have a meticulous concern for their patient's needs:
EPIDEMICS VI, Section 4, Ch. 7: *"Kindnesses to those who are ill. For example to do in a clean way his food or drink or whatever he sees, softly what he touches. Things that do no great harm and are easily got, such as cool drink where it is needed. Entrance, conversation. Position and clothing for the sick person, hair, nails, scents"* (Loeb, Vol. VII, pp249,251).

Medical ethics and etiquette

Ethics

Undoubtedly, the most famous part of the Hippocratic Corpus is The Oath. However, it is very important to bear in mind that many other parts of the Corpus are concerned with medical ethics. With regard to the Hippocratic Oath, very few physicians have ever seen the original, and The Oath given to students at some medical schools (rarely done these days) is a watered-down version of the original. You will see why:
The Oath: *"I swear by Apollo Physician, by Asclepius, by Health, by Panacea and by all the gods and goddesses, making them my witnesses, that I will carry out, according to my ability and judgement, this oath and this indenture. To hold my teacher in this art equal to my own parents; to make him partner in my livelihood; when he is in need of money to share mine with him; to consider his family as my own brothers, and to teach them this art, if they want to learn it, without fee or indenture; to impart precept, oral instruction, and all other instruction to my own sons, the sons of my teacher, and to indentured pupils who have taken the physician's oath, but to nobody else. I will use treatment to help the sick according to my ability and judgement, but never with a view to injury and wrong-doing. Neither will I administer a poison to anybody when asked to do so, nor will I suggest such a course. Similarly I will not give to a woman a pessary to cause abortion. But I will keep pure and holy both my life and my art. I will not use the knife, not even, verily, on sufferers from stone, but I will give place to such as are craftsmen therein. Into whatsoever houses I enter, I will enter to help the sick, and I will abstain from all intentional wrong-doing and harm, especially from*

Figure 2. Fragment of Hippocratic Oath, third century A.D. Oxyrhynchus papyrus no. 2547. Reprinted with the kind permission of the Wellcome Institute Library, London.

abusing the bodies of man or woman, bond or free. And whatsoever I shall see or hear in the course of my profession, as well as outside my profession in my intercourse with men, if it be what should not be published abroad, I will never divulge, holding such things to be holy secrets. Now if I carry out this oath, and break it not, may I gain for ever reputation among all men for my life and for my art; but if I transgress it and forswear myself, may the opposite befall me" (Loeb, Vol. I, pp299, 301).

There are some admirable and highly principled admonitions here: to avoid intentional wrong-doing, to abstain from sexual relations with patients, to consider the consultation with the patient as a matter of absolute confidentiality and, above all, to strive for the patient's benefit. The very existence of The Oath is an admirable thing, and speaks well for the moral climate in which the Hippocratic doctors practised. However, some aspects of The Oath are clearly no longer relevant to current circumstances. The exclusion of surgeons as unworthy members of the profession and the exclusion of women as suitable trainee physicians would alienate a large part of the modern medical profession! Similarly, the solemn requirement to share one's money with one's teachers is something that today's students would regard as absurd. The prohibition on euthanasia and abortion is interesting. These are of course controversial issues in modern times, and whether or not they were controversial in Hippocratic times is difficult to tell. Their inclusion in The Oath suggests that controversy might have existed.

Certainly, methods for procuring abortion were known, as is shown from a passage where aborted embryos and foetuses were carefully scrutinized for the development of recognizable features:

FLESHES, Ch. 19: *"To begin with, when the seed arrives in the uterus, in seven days it has all the parts the body is to have*. You might wonder how I know this: well, I have learned much in the following way. The common prostitutes, who have frequent experience in these matters, after having been with a man know when they have become pregnant, and then destroy the child. When it has been destroyed, it drops out like a piece of flesh. If you put this flesh into water and examine it in the water, you will see that it has all the parts: the orbits of the eyes, the ears and the limbs; the fingers, the legs, the feet, the toes, and the genital parts, and all the rest of the body is distinct"* (Loeb, Vol. VIII, pp159,161).

The Oath specifically prohibits intentional wrong-doing in two separate passages. However, the famous medical dictum—above all to do no harm—is not really covered. "Primum non nocere", as it is sometimes rendered, is not about intentional wrong-doing. It concerns the balancing of possible harmful and beneficial effects of any intended therapy, and striving to avoid any possible harm. I found advice to this effect in Epidemics I:

EPIDEMICS I, Ch. XI: *"As to diseases, make a habit of two things - to help, or at least to do no harm. The art has three factors, the disease, the patient, the physician. The physician is the servant of the art"* (Loeb, Vol. I, p165).

Here is a piece from Physician, which echoes some of the sentiments in The Oath:

PHYSICIAN, Ch. 1: *"In every social relation he will be fair, for fairness must be of great service. The intimacy also between physician and patient is close. Patients in fact put themselves into*

---

*The description is, of course, of an embryo far more advanced than 7 days *the hands of their physician, and at every moment he meets women, maidens, and possessions very precious indeed. So towards all these self-control must be used. Such then should the physician be, in body and in soul"* (Loeb, Vol. VIII, pp301,303).

Fees

Medicine in classical Greece was a fee-for-service profession, but the students were advised to put financial considerations second to patient care. There were two such admonitions, both in Precepts:

PRECEPTS, Ch. IV: *"This piece of advice also will need our consideration, as it contributes somewhat to the whole. For should you begin by discussing fees, you will suggest to the patient either that you will go away and leave him if no agreement be reached, or that you will neglect him and not prescribe any immediate treatment. So one must not be anxious about fixing a fee. For I consider such a worry to be harmful to a troubled patient, particularly if the disease be acute. For the quickness of the disease, offering no opportunity for turning back, spurs on the good physician not to seek his profit but rather to lay hold on reputation. Therefore it is better to reproach a patient you have saved than to extort money from those who are at death's door"* (Loeb, Vol. 1, p317).

PRECEPTS, Ch. VI: *"I urge you not to be too unkind, but to consider carefully your patient's superabundance or means. Sometimes give your services for nothing, calling to mind a previous benefaction or present satisfaction. And if there be an opportunity of serving one who is a stranger in financial straits, give full assistance to all such. For where there is love of man, there is also love of the art"* (Loeb, Vol. I, p319).

Consultation with colleagues

Consultation with other physicians was strongly recommended:

PRECEPTS, Ch. VIII: *"A physician does not violate etiquette even if, being in difficulties on occasion over a patient and in the dark through inexperience, he should urge the calling in of others, in order to learn by consultation the truth about the case, and in order that there may be fellow-workers to afford abundant help"* (Loeb, Vol. I, p323).

However, the excesses of some ward rounds should be avoided (if possible!):

PRECEPTS, Ch. VIII: *"Physicians who meet in consultation must never quarrel, or jeer at one another. For I will assert upon oath, a* *physician's reasoning should never be jealous of another. To be so will be a sign of weakness. Those who act thus lightly are rather those connected with the business of the market-place. Yet it is no mistaken idea to call in a consultant. For in all abundance there is lack*"* (Loeb, Vol. I, p325).

The working environment of the Hippocratic doctor

As suggested in The Oath, training was by apprenticeship, and presumably at the discretion of the physician/teacher. Doctors might frequently have had their students with them, and the students seem to have been involved in patient care, as suggested by the following piece:

DECORUM, Ch. XVII: *"Let one of your pupils be left in charge, to carry out instructions without unpleasantness, and to administer the treatment. Choose out those who have been already admitted into the mysteries of the art, so as to add anything necessary, and to give treatment with safety. He is there also to prevent those things escaping notice that happen in the intervals between visits. Never put a layman in charge of anything, otherwise if a mischance occur the blame will fall on you"* (Loeb, Vol. II, p299).

There were probably no compulsory subjects for study, no formal examinations and no register of medical practitioners. Deciding who was and who was not a 'doctor' was probably not a straightforward exercise for potential patients. The existence of incompetent doctors, impostors and charlatans has been alluded to already, and there are many references to this sort of thing in the Corpus. Here are two examples:

THE SACRED DISEASE†, Ch. I: *"My own view is that those who first attributed a sacred character to this malady were like the magicians, purifiers, charlatans and quacks of our own day, men who claim great piety and superior knowledge"* (Loeb, Vol. II, p141)

PRECEPTS, Ch. VII: *"For quacks do not attempt treatment when they see an alarming condition, and avoid calling in other physicians, because they wickedly hate help"* (Loeb, Vol. I, p321).

There is a particularly bitter attack on those perceived as charlatans in Laws, the author clearly wishing for the existence of a regulatory body with punitive powers (such as the General Medical Council in the United Kingdom):

*One can never have enough good advice
†Epilepsy

LAWS, Ch. I: *"Medicine is the most distinguished of all the arts, but through the ignorance of those who practise it, and of those who casually judge such practitioners, it is now of all the arts by far the least esteemed. The chief reason for this error seems to me to be this: medicine is the only art which our states have made subject to no penalty save that of dishonour, and dishonour does not wound those are compacted of it. Such men in fact are very like the supernumeraries in tragedies. Just as these have the appearance, dress and mask of an actor without being actors, so too with physicians; many are physicians by repute, very few are such in reality"* (Loeb, Vol. II, p263).

However, it would seem that physicians might have had good cause to be wary of patients' dissatisfaction with their treatment. The author of Ancient Medicine, again mercilessly castigating incompetent doctors, indicated that retribution for bad doctors was sometimes exacted by patients:

ANCIENT MEDICINE, Ch. IX: *"For most physicians seem to me to be in the same case as bad pilots; the mistakes of the latter are unnoticed so long as they are steering in a calm, but when a great storm overtakes them with a violent gale, all men realise clearly then that it is their ignorance and blundering which have lost the ship. So also when bad physicians, who comprise the great majority, treat men who are suffering from no serious complaint, so that the greatest of blunders would not affect them seriously— such illnesses occur very often, being far more common than serious disease—they are not shown up in their true colours to laymen if their errors are confined to such cases; but when they meet with a severe, violent and dangerous illness, then it is that their errors and want of skill are manifest to all. The punishment of the impostor, whether sailor or doctor, is not postponed, but follows speedily"* (Loeb, Vol. I, pp28,29).

The problem with this, of course, is that the patient's perceptions might be distorted, and everyone will notice here a good description of the ungrateful patient:

DISEASES I, Ch. 8: *"Generally speaking, people blame the physician, in diseases and wounds, even for the evils that follow of necessity from other evils, when these occur, not recognizing the constraint that makes such things happen. If he attends a patient with a fever or a wound, and fails at first to help him by his administration, but on the next day the patient is worse, people blame the physician; but if he does help the patient, people do not praise him in due proportion, for they hold the patient's improvement to have been a matter of course"* (Loeb, Vol. V, p119).

A particularly interesting aspect of ancient medical practice was that many physicians probably travelled from town to town, seeking patients. This was presumably because most towns were very small, and provided insufficient patients for a doctor to make a reasonable living. On the other hand, the treatments outlined in many parts of the Corpus involved many weeks or months of medical attention, and it might have been the case that physicians travelled on a regular basis to local towns near their home. The fact that physicians tended to travel is suggested by several passages in the Corpus, including the following:

LAWS, Ch. IV: *"These are the conditions that we must allow the art of medicine, and we must acquire of it a real knowledge before we travel from city to city and win the reputation of being physicians not only in word but also in deed"* (Loeb, Vol. II, p265).

AIRS WATERS PLACES, Ch. 1: *"Therefore, on arrival at a town with which he is unfamiliar, a physician should examine its position with respect to the winds and to the risings of the sun"* (Loeb, Vol. I, p71).

Chapter 4

The Hippocratic tradition of rational medicine

For mere humans to assume that, through knowledge, they might favourably intervene in the course of a disease, was a major conceptual leap from praying or offering sacrifices for a favourable outcome. It is this rational attitude which distinguishes the Hippocratic doctor from other healers of his time and which is the basis for the claim that modern medicine traces its intellectual lineage back to the Hippocratic tradition.

Curiously enough, however, many of the treatments available to Hippocratic doctors (apart mainly from the treatment of trauma and the drainage of abscesses) we would today regard as quackery. What we have to remember is that the Hippocratic doctors were responding to the imperative of allaying the suffering of patients whose diseases they could not hope to understand. They were treating thalassaemia long before oxygen, red blood cells, and the circulation of the blood were discovered, let alone before the molecular basis of the haemoglobinopathies was known. Doing nothing was not an option. What was important, and distinguished the Hippocratic doctors, was their attitude to disease. They regarded diseases as having natural causes, and considered that treatment should be based on reason and experience, not superstition and religion.

For example, the author of The Sacred Disease (i.e. epilepsy) begins his treatise:

THE SACRED DISEASE, Ch. I: *"I am about to discuss the disease called 'sacred'. It is not, in my opinion, any more divine or more sacred than other diseases, but has a natural cause, and its supposed divine origin is due to men's inexperience, and to their wonder at its peculiar character"* (Loeb, Vol. II, p139).

The author of Ancient Medicine praised the rational enquiries of his predecessors (his ancient medicine!) in the following words:

ANCIENT MEDICINE, Ch. XII: *"I declare, however, that we ought not to reject the ancient art as non-existent, or on the ground that its method of inquiry is faulty, just because it has not attained exactness in every detail, but much rather, because it has been able by reasoning to rise from deep ignorance to approximately perfect accuracy, I think we ought to admire the discoveries as the work, not of chance, but of inquiry rightly and correctly conducted"* (Loeb, Vol. I, p33).

An attempt to define a logical method of inquiry is given by the author of Epidemics VI:

EPIDEMICS VI, Section 3, Ch. 12: *"The summary conclusion comes from the origin and the going forth, and from very many accounts and things learned little by little, when one gathers them together and studies them thoroughly, whether the things are like one another; again whether the dissimilarities in them are like each other, so that from dissimilarities there arises one similarity. This would be the road (i.e . . . method). In this way develop verification of correct accounts and refutation of erroneous ones"* (Loeb, Vol. VII, pp239,241).

Here are three other examples:

PRECEPTS, Ch. I: *"Healing is a matter of time, but it is sometimes also a matter of opportunity. However, knowing this, one must attend in medical practice not primarily to plausible theories, but to experience combined with reason"* (Loeb, Vol. I, p313).

PRECEPTS, Ch. II: *". . . conclusions which are merely verbal cannot bear fruit, only those do which are based on demonstrated fact. For affirmation and talk are deceptive and treacherous. Wherefore one must hold fast to facts in generalisations also, and occupy oneself with facts persistently, if one is to acquire that ready and infallible habit which we call 'the art of medicine'"* (Loeb, Vol. I, p315).

ANCIENT MEDICINE, Ch. XX: *"I also hold that clear knowledge about natural science can be acquired from medicine and from no other source, and that one can attain this knowledge when medicine itself has been properly comprehended, but till then it is quite impossible—I mean to possess this information, what man is, by what causes he is made, and similar points accurately. Since this at least I think a physician must know, and be at great pains to know, about natural science, if he is going to perform aught of his duty, what man is in relation to foods and drinks, and to habits generally, and what will be the effects of each on each individual. It is not sufficient to learn simply that cheese is a bad food, as it gives a pain to one who eats a surfeit of it; we must know what the pain is, the reasons for it, and which constituent of man is harmfully affected"* (Loeb, Vol. I, pp53,55).

As in any multi-author volume, not all hold the same view. In response to 'good' or 'bad' signs in dreams, the author of Regimen IV makes the following proposals:

REGIMEN IV, Ch. LXXXIX: *"So with this knowledge about the heavenly bodies, precautions must be taken, with change of regimen and prayers to the gods; in the case of good signs, to the Sun, to Heavenly Zeus, to Zeus, Protector of Home, to Athena, Protectress of Home, to Hermes and to Apollo; in the case of adverse signs, to the Averters of evil, to Earth and to the Heroes, that all dangers may be averted"* (Loeb, Vol. IV, p437).

However, the advice in the preceding quotation is very much out of character with the rest of the Corpus. It is of much greater significance, when discussing rationality, to note that there exists in many parts of the Corpus an almost superstitious attitude to the seasons, to wind direction, and to periodicity of symptoms, especially fevers. Although the incidence of some diseases can obviously be influenced by the seasons, and might just possibly be independently influenced by wind direction, it is clear that a total break with irrationality was as difficult in Hippocratic times as it is now. For example:

AIRS WATERS PLACES, Ch. XI: *"One should be especially on one's guard against the most violent changes of the seasons, and unless compelled one should neither purge, nor apply cautery or knife to the bowels, before at least ten days are past. The following are the four most violent changes and the most dangerous:- both solstices, especially the summer solstice, both the equinoxes, so reckoned, especially the autumnal. One must also guard against the risings of the stars, especially of the Dog Star, then of Arcturus, and also of the setting of the Pleiades. For it is especially at these times that diseases come to a crisis. Some prove fatal, some come to an end, all others change to another form and another constitution"* (Loeb, Vol. I, p105).

APHORISMS, Third section, Ch. V: *"South winds cause deafness, dimness of vision, heaviness of the head, torpor, and are relaxing. When such winds prevail, their characteristics extend to sufferers from illnesses. A north wind causes coughs, sore throats, constipation, difficult micturition accompanied by shivering, pains in the sides and chest; such are the symptoms one must expect in illnesses when the wind prevails"* (Loeb, Vol. IV, p123).

The irrational and pervasive concept of periodicity is interesting, and probably had its origin in the high prevalence of malaria in ancient Greece. Certain species of the malaria parasite (e.g. *Plasmodium vivax* and *Plasmodium malariae*) give rise to regular and highly predictable bouts of fever, in between which the patient's temperature is normal. In any case, here is a typical example of a groundless concern for periodicity:

PRORRHETIC I, Ch. 14: *"For a fever to begin in head wounds on the fourth, seventh, or eleventh days is especially deadly. The crisis occurs in most cases, if the fever began on the fourth day after the wound, towards the eleventh day; if the person became febrile on the seventh day, towards the fourteenth or seventeenth; if the person first had fever on the eleventh day, then towards the twentieth day, just as was described for fevers arising without visible causes"* (Loeb, Vol. VIII, p255).

Chapter 5

Hippocratic ideas of health and disease

On matters of ethics and morals, and such things as dreams, we and the ancient doctors speak to each other on equal terms. Their knowledge and opinions are as valuable and as valid as ours. When we move to trauma, and the treatment of fractures and dislocations, we can still speak to each other with little difficulty. A broken femur is, after all, clearly a broken femur and one does not need advanced molecular biology or complicated laboratory tests to either make the correct diagnosis or devise an effective treatment. However, when we come to non-trauma medicine, the gulf of knowledge between us and the Hippocratic doctors is vast. We must try to view the human body and the patient's illness through the eyes of someone almost entirely devoid of scientific knowledge, and whose concepts are based largely on conjecture.

WHS Jones, in his Introduction to Volume I of the Loeb series on Hippocrates, put it perfectly in 1923: "We have learned to associate, almost by instinct, the science of medicine with bacteria, with chemistry, with clinical thermometers, disinfectants and all the apparatus of careful nursing. All such associations, if we wish even dimly to appreciate the work of Hippocrates and of his predecessors, we must endeavour to break; we must unthink the greater part of those habits of thought which education has made second nature". Almost 80 years later, we would cite magnetic resonance imaging, gene therapy and keyhole surgery as the obstacles to our understanding of Hippocratic medicine. Clearly, we have a great deal more to unthink!

Conversely, it is important also to note that we are now no longer aware of the natural history of many diseases, because of early and effective intervention. For example, among the several descriptions of jaundice (especially in Internal Affections), there presumably exist cases of obstructive jaundice from a gallstone in the common bile duct. Without effective surgical intervention, how do these patients fare, and which is the appropriate description? For this, and other conditions, it is often difficult to be sure.

Hippocratic concepts of health and disease

The basic premise on which much of the Corpus is based is that the body consists of four humours (or fluids) and that they must be completely mingled with one another for a state of health. The four humours are blood, phlegm, bile and black bile. The precise nature of black bile is uncertain, but presumably refers to blood mixed with vomit or fluid faeces. Here it is in the words of a Hippocratic doctor:

NATURE OF MAN, Ch. IV: *"The body of man has in itself blood, phlegm, yellow bile and black bile; these make up the nature of his body, and through these he feels pain or enjoys health. Now he enjoys the most perfect health when these elements are duly proportioned to one another in respect of compounding, power and bulk, and when they are perfectly mingled. Pain is felt when one of these elements is in defect or excess, or is isolated in the body without being compounded with all the others. For when an element is isolated and stands by itself, not only must the place which it left become diseased, but the place where it stands in a flood must, because of the excess, cause pain and distress"* (Loeb, Vol. IV, pp11,13).

Precisely how disease (i.e. the separating out of individual humours) is precipitated is not clear, but is seen almost always as a consequence of the lack of balance in the opposing qualities of hot and cold, dry and moist. Very frequently, inappropriate diet or exercise were seen as precipitating disease. Here is how the ancients put it:

AFFECTIONS, Ch. 1: *"... all human diseases arise from bile and phlegm; the bile and phlegm produce diseases when, inside the body, one of them becomes too moist, too dry, too hot, or too cold; they become this way from foods and drinks, from exertions and wounds, from smell, sound, sight, and venery, and from heat and cold; this happens when any of the things mentioned are applied to the body at the wrong time, against custom, in too great amount and too strong, or in insufficient amount and too weak"* (Loeb, Vol. V, p7).

INTERNAL AFFECTIONS, Ch. 44: *"The following diseases are called ileuses. They arise, in most cases, from the following: if, in winter, a person employs a hot, moist diet and does not exercise by taking walks in accordance with his food but goes to bed in a full state, and is then suddenly obliged to walk a long distance when it is cold, and then gets chilled to the bone, he suffers the following: ... "* (Loeb, Vol. VI, p219).

ANCIENT MEDICINE, Ch. XVI: *"And I believe that of all the powers none hold less sway in the body than cold and heat. My reasons are these. So long as the hot and cold in the body are mixed up together, they cause no pain. For the hot is tempered and moderated by the cold, and the cold by the hot. But when*

either is entirely separated from the other, then it causes pain"
(Loeb, Vol. I, p43).

The author of Regimen I in essence considered disease as a problem of homeostasis. For example, if we eat just a half slice of bread too much or too little per day, in the course of a thousand days, that will make a big difference. He put it thus:
REGIMEN I, Ch. II: *"In fact, if there occur even a small deficiency of one or the other (i.e. diet or exercise) in course of time the body must be overwhelmed by the excess and fall sick"* (Loeb, Vol. IV, p231).

However, uniquely among the treatises, the author of Breaths had a different view. He was clearly fascinated by the fact that the sustenance of life required the constant drawing in of air into the body. For us it is straightforward, in that we can say that we need a constant supply of oxygen for the survival of the body's cells (especially those of the brain). Here is how he put it:
BREATHS, Ch. III: *"Now bodies, of men and of animals generally, are nourished by three kinds of nourishment, and the names thereof are solid food, drink, and wind. Wind in bodies is called breath, outside bodies it is called air. It is the most powerful of all and in all, and it is worth while examining its power"* (Loeb, Vol. II, pp229,231).

BREATHS, Ch IV: *"So great is the need of wind for all bodies that while a man can be deprived of everything else, both food and drink, for two, three, or more days, and live, yet if the wind passages into the body be cut off he will die in a brief part of a day, showing that the greatest need for a body is wind. Moreover, all other activities of a man are intermittent, for life is full of changes; but breathing is continuous for all mortal creatures, inspiration and expiration being alternate"* (Loeb, Vol. II, pp231,233).

He then goes on to state that all diseases arise from the air (although the subsequent arguments are not particularly strong):
BREATHS, Ch. V: *"Now I have said that all animals participate largely in air. So after this I must say that it is likely that maladies occur from this source and from no other. On the subject as a whole I have said sufficient; after this I will by the same reasoning proceed to facts and show that diseases are all the offspring of air"* (Loeb, Vol. II, p233).

It is worth briefly examining the concept of the mingling and balance of humours, which corresponds to the state of health. You will see from Table 2 that, for example, an explanation for the

TABLE 2. Contrasting explanations of modern and Hippocratic medicine for some common phenomena

Mucus secretion

Modern:	Produced *de novo* by glands
Hippocratic:	Separates out from the otherwise perfect mingling of humours

Warmth at the site of skin infection

Modern:	Vasodilatation, raising local skin temperature closer to core body temperature
Hippocratic:	Heat separates out

Cold extremities in rigors

Modern:	Peripheral vasoconstriction, reducing the flow of warm blood
Hippocratic:	Cold separates out

appearance of mucus is for us simple—it is produced *de novo* by glands. But in the absence of this knowledge, it is not a bad explanation that it separates out from an otherwise perfectly mingled state in the body.

The recovery of health required that the separated, unbalanced humours be brought together once again into a state of harmonious blending. This process has been described as 'coction'. It is a matter of particular importance to note that the process of coction was considered to leave a residue, which had to be evacuated. The Hippocratic doctors attached great weight to the evacuation of this residue, which could be effected by any of the normal or abnormal bodily secretions (e.g. sweat, urine, pus). It is perhaps for this reason that, throughout the Corpus, nose bleeds (curiously from our point of view) were regarded as beneficial and the use of emetics and enemas was widespread. For example:

REGIMEN IN ACUTE DISEASES (APPENDIX), Ch. 1: *"If blood flows from the nose, the affection is resolved; also if true critical sweats supervene, accompanied by thick white urines having a fine sediment, and also if an abscess forms anywhere. If it is resolved without these, there will be a recurrence of the ailment, or pain in the hip or legs will follow. If a patient is going to recover, he will also expectorate thick sputa"* (Loeb, Vol. VI, pp263,265).

The other important concept is that of 'critical' days. These were specific days following the onset of the illness on which coction occurred, and the patient recovered. If coction did not occur, the disease persisted. Here is one of many examples, illustrating the previously noted irrational importance attached to timing:

APHORISMS IV, Number XXXVI: *"Sweats in a fever case are beneficial if they begin on the third day, the fifth, the seventh, the ninth, the eleventh, the fourteenth, the seventeenth, the twenty-first, the twenty-seventh, the thirty-first and the thirty-fourth, for these sweats bring diseases to a crisis. Sweats occurring on other days indicate pain, a long disease and relapses"* (Loeb, Vol. IV, p145).

Hippocratic approach to the patient

Modern medicine is geared overwhelmingly to making a diagnosis of the patient's ailment, and from the diagnosis flows the required treatment and the prognosis. From our vantage point, we know that, for the large majority of diseases, any attempt by the Hippocratic doctors to make a meaningful diagnosis was futile, since they knew essentially no basic science and no pathology. Whether or not the ancients were instinctively conscious of this problem is difficult to say. Certainly, they had their own ideas of bodily functions, although they were often bizarre (e.g. the flow of blood, bile, phlegm and air in the veins). Nevertheless, the Hippocratic school aimed not at diagnosis but at establishing prognosis, thereby (wisely) avoiding the quagmire into which they would otherwise usually have fallen. There are three long treatises on prognosis. The author of Prognostic put their position extremely well in his opening chapter:

PROGNOSTIC, Ch. I: *"I hold that it is an excellent thing for a physician to practise forecasting. For if he discover and declare unaided by the side of his patients the present, the past and the future, and fill in the gaps in the account given by the sick, he will be the more believed to understand the cases, so that men will confidently entrust themselves to him for treatment. Furthermore, he will carry out the treatment best if he know beforehand from the present symptoms what will take place later"* (Loeb, Vol. II, p7).

By precise forecasting of the problems to come, the Hippocratic doctor felt that he could better prepare himself to deal with them. Interestingly, he also saw accurate forecasting (and also accurate descriptions of what had already happened to the patient, before being told by the patient) as an important way of gaining the patient's confidence: an important factor for itinerant doctors needing to establish their legitimacy.

The Hippocratic doctor had at his disposal only the patient's history and the physical examination. No laboratory tests! Even the physical examination was limited. One has to remember, for example, that temperature could be measured only by touch. The clinical significance of the pulse is said not to have been widely understood until after the Hippocratic Corpus was written. Measurement of the pulse was apparently popularized by Herophilus of Chalcedon (c. 330–260 BC), who devised a portable water clock with which to time his patients' pulses[11]. However, it is worth noting that the authors of Epidemics IV and Epidemics V were clearly aware of the pulse and its significance. The pulse is mentioned several times in his Epidemics IV, and here are two examples:

EPIDEMICS IV, Ch. 20b: *"In the most severe fevers the pulse is strongest and most frequent"* (Loeb, Vol. VII, p109).

EPIDEMICS IV, Ch. 23: *"Zoilus the carpenter had a sluggish trembling pulse"* (Loeb, Vol. VII, p115).

It is especially curious therefore, that there is no detailed and systematic instruction on how to take the patient's history or how to conduct the physical examination. One of the few examples, on how to detect lack of sight in a confused patient, is as follows:

INTERNAL AFFECTIONS, Ch. 48: *"The pupils of the eyes are dilated, the patient sees dimly, and if you bring your finger up to his eyes, he does not perceive it, because he cannot see; this is how you can tell that he does not see: he does not blink when the finger is brought near"* (Loeb, Vol. VI, p233).

On the other hand, very detailed descriptions of urine, faeces, vomit and sputum are given with equally detailed advice on the prognostic significance for the patient of various aspects of these body fluids. The prognostic significance seems grossly overstated. Here are some examples:

PROGNOSTIC, Ch. XII: *"Urine is best when the sediment is white, smooth and even for the whole period of the illness until the crisis, for it indicates a short sickness and a sure recovery. But should the sediment intermit, and the urine sometimes be clear and sometimes show the white, smooth, even deposit, the illness will be longer and recovery less likely. Should the urine be reddish and the sediment reddish and smooth, recovery will be sure, although the illness will be longer than in the former case. Sediments in urine which are like coarse meal are bad, and even worse than these are flaky sediments. Thin, white sediments are very bad, and even worse than these are those like bran. Clouds suspended in the urine are good when white but bad when black. So long as the urine is thin and of a yellowish-red colour, it is a sign that the disease is unconcocted; and if the disease should also be protracted, while the urine is of this nature, there is a danger lest the patient will not be able to hold out until the disease is concocted. The more fatal kinds of urine are the fetid, watery, black and thick; for men and women black urine is the worst, for children watery urine"* (Loeb, Vol. II, p25,27).

PROGNOSTIC, Ch. XIII: *"That vomit is most useful which is most thoroughly compounded of phlegm and bile, and it must not be thick nor brought up in too great quantity. Less compounded vomits are worse. And if that which is brought up be of the colour of leeks, or livid, or black, in all cases vomit of these colours must be considered bad. If the same patient brings up vomit of all these colours, he is quite at death's door. Of the vomits, the livid indicates the earliest death, should the odour be foul; but all odours which are rather putrid and foul are bad in the case of all vomits"* (Loeb, Vol. II, p29).

PROGNOSTIC, Ch. XIV: *"Sputum, in all pains of the lungs and ribs, should be quickly and easily brought up, and the yellow should appear thoroughly compounded with the sputum; for if long after the beginning of the pain yellow sputum should be coughed up, or reddish-yellow, or causing much coughing, or not thoroughly compounded; it is rather a bad sign. For yellow sputum, uncompounded, is dangerous, and the white, viscous and round bodes no good. Pale green, if pronounced, and frothy sputum is also bad. If it should be so uncompounded as to appear actually black, this is a more alarming sign than the others"* (Loeb, Vol. II, p29).

Chapter 6

Some ancient case histories and disease descriptions

Some diseases have highly characteristic symptoms, and can therefore easily be identified by clinical history alone. It was interesting to come across such conditions, described by doctors and suffered by patients in precisely the same way in ancient as in modern times. These descriptions provide a powerful link with the past. It was also very interesting, and moving, to read the ancient clinical case histories, and to relive individual battles of life and death from the distant past. I have therefore included a selection of case histories and disease descriptions in this chapter.

Tetanus

There are several descriptions of tetanus in the Corpus, so it might have been moderately common in ancient times. The disease is now rare (at least in economically developed countries) mainly because of extensive vaccination programmes. Here is a general description of tetanus, and a case history following a crush injury:

DISEASES III, Ch. 12: *"When tetanus occurs, the jaws become as hard as wood, and patients cannot open their mouths. Their eyes shed tears and look awry, their backs become rigid, and they cannot adduct their legs; similarly, not their arms either. The patient's face becomes red, he suffers great pain and, when he is on the point of death, he vomits drink, gruel and phlegm through his nostrils. This patient generally dies on the third, fifth, seventh or fourteenth day; if he survives for that many, he recovers"* (Loeb, Vol. VI, p25).

EPIDEMICS V, Ch. 74: *"The commander of the large ship; the anchor crushed his forefinger and the one below it on the right hand. Inflammation developed, gangrene, and fever. He was purged moderately. Mild fevers and pain. Part of the finger fell away. After the seventh day satisfactory serum came out. After that, problems with the tongue: he said he could not articulate everything. Prediction made: that* opisthotonos *would come. His jaws became fixed together, then it went to the neck, on the third day he was entirely convulsed backward, with sweating. On the sixth day after the prediction he died"* (Loeb, Vol. VII, p203).

A case of puerperal fever

Infection of the womb following the birth of a child was a dreaded, relatively common and frequently fatal complication of pregnancy until modern times. There are several descriptions of puerperal fever in the Corpus, and here is one of the untold number of tragedies, fortunately rare since the advent of antibiotics:

EPIDEMICS III, Case XII: *"A woman who lay sick by the Liars' Market, after giving birth in a first and painful delivery to a male child, was seized with fever. From the very first there was thirst, nausea, slight pain at the stomach, dry tongue, bowels disordered with thin and scanty discharges, no sleep.*

Second day. Slight rigor; acute fever; slight, cold sweating around the head.

Third day. In pain; crude, thin, copious discharges from bowels.

Fourth day. Rigor; general exacerbation; sleepless.

Fifth day. In pain.

Sixth day. The same symptoms; copious, fluid discharges from the bowels.

Seventh day. Rigor; acute fever; thirst; much tossing; towards evening cold sweat all over; chill; extremities cold, and would not be warmed. At night she again had a rigor; the extremities would not be warmed; no sleep; slight delirium, but quickly was rational again.

Eighth day. About mid-day recovered her heat; thirst; coma; nausea; vomited bilious, scanty, yellowish matters. An uncomfortable night; no sleep; unconsciously passed a copious discharge of urine.

Ninth day. General abatement of the symptoms; coma. Towards evening slight rigor; vomited scanty, bilious matters.

Tenth day. Rigor; exacerbation of the fever; no sleep whatsoever. In the early morning a copious discharge of urine without sediment; extremities were warmed.

Eleventh day. Vomited bilious matters, of the colour of verdigris. A rigor shortly afterwards, and the extremities became cold again; in the evening sweat, rigor and copious vomiting; a painful night.

Twelfth day. Vomited copious, black, fetid matters; much hiccoughing; painful thirst.

Thirteenth day. Vomited black, fetid, copious matters; rigor. About mid-day lost her speech.

Fourteenth day. Epistaxis; death.

The bowels of this patient were throughout loose, and there were shivering fits. Age about seventeen" (Loeb, Vol. I, pp237,239).

Migraine

Sufferers of migraine will recognize here a fairly classical description of migraine, with preliminary visual symptoms, followed by severe local and then generalized headache, and vomiting. It is interesting that the symptom complex has remained unchanged for over 2,500 years, and presumably therefore for very much longer.

EPIDEMICS V, Ch. 83: *"Phoenix's problem: he seemed to see flashes like lightning in his eye, usually the right. And when he had suffered that a short time a terrible pain developed towards his right temple, then in the whole head, and then into the part of the neck where the head is attached to the vertebra behind, and there was stretching and hardness around the teeth. He kept trying to open them, straining. Vomits, whenever they occurred, averted the pains I have described, and made them more gentle"* (Loeb, Vol. VII, p207).

Mental and psychosomatic disorders

Mental illness does not occupy a prominent place in the Corpus. However, depression is briefly mentioned on many occasions suggesting that it might have been a common condition in ancient times. Certainly, Hippocratic doctors were clearly aware of the powerful influences which the mind can exert over the body. Here are two references to depression, the first with a rather fanciful description of the precipitating factors:

AIRS WATERS PLACES, Ch. X: *"But if the weather be northerly and dry, with no rain either during the Dog Star or at Arcturus, it is very beneficial to those who have a phlegmatic or humid constitution, and to women, but it is very harmful to the bilious. For these dry up overmuch, and are attacked by dry ophthalmia and by acute, protracted fevers, in some cases too by melancholies"* (Loeb, Vol. I, p103).

APHORISMS, SECTION VI, NUMBER 23: *"Fear or depression that is prolonged means melancholia"* (Loeb, Vol. IV, p185).

There is also a reference to manic depression:

EPIDEMICS V, Ch. 84: *"Parmeniscus previously was visited by depressions and desire to end his life, but sometimes again with optimism"* (Loeb, Vol. VII, p209).

Here are descriptions of two phobias:

EPIDEMICS V, Ch. 82: *"Democles, who was with him, seemed blind and powerless of body, and could not go along a cliff, nor on to a bridge to cross a ditch of the least depth, but he could go through the ditch itself. This affected him for some time"* (Loeb, Vol. VII, p207).

EPIDEMICS V, Ch. 81: *"Nicanor's affection, when he went to a drinking party, was fear of the flute girl. Whenever he heard the voice of the flute begin to play at a symposium, masses of terrors rose up. He said that he could hardly bear it when it was night, but if he heard it in the daytime he was not affected. Such symptoms persisted over a long period of time"* (Loeb, Vol. VII, p207).

The possibility that physical symptoms could be caused by the patient's mental condition is mentioned on a couple of occasions, including the following:

REGIMEN IN ACUTE DISEASES (APPENDIX), Ch. 40: *"If the body is weakened, if there is pain in the head, if the ears or the nose are stopped, or if there is ptyalism, heaviness of the knees, or fullness of the body beyond what is normal, give hellebore, provided that the condition is not the result of drink, venery, grief, anxiety or sleeplessness; if the condition has one of these as its cause, let the treatment be directed against that"* (Loeb, Vol. VI, p305).

Arthritis

It is interesting to note that the ancient doctors had an accurate concept of normal joint function:

PLACES IN MAN, Ch. 7: *"Fluid is present naturally in all the joints, and when it is clean the joints are healthy, and for this reason they move easily and their members slip smoothly over one another. Difficulty and pain arise when moisture flows out of tissue that has been damaged in some way. First, the joint becomes fixed, since the moisture flowing into it from the tissue is not slippery"* (Loeb, Vol. VIII, pp35,37).

Of the various forms of arthritis, it is difficult to know which were most prevalent in Hippocratic times. Life expectancy was probably too short to allow osteoarthritis to develop in a significant proportion of the population. Gout is mentioned in Affections:

AFFECTIONS, Ch. 31: *"Gout is the most violent of all such conditions of the joints, as well as the most chronic and intractable"* (Loeb, Vol. V, p55).

That the ancient diagnosis of gout probably corresponds to the modern one is suggested by the correct age and sex incidence ascribed to gout. Unlike rheumatoid arthritis, it is a disease of the older male, a fact colourfully expressed in Aphorisms:

APHORISMS, SECTION VI, Numbers XXVIII to XXX:
"XXVIII. Eunuchs neither get gout nor grow bald.
XXIX. A woman does not get gout unless menstruation is suppressed.
XXX. A youth does not get gout before sexual intercourse" (Loeb, Vol. IV, p187).

Clubbing of the fingers and toes

Every medical student quickly learns to recognize clubbing of the nails of the fingers and toes. It is a very curious condition, caused by raising of the nail bed, and is found in a variety of chronic conditions, especially suppurative affections of the lung and cyanotic heart disease. It was well recognized by Hippocratic doctors, and is mentioned several times in the Corpus, including the following:

DISEASES II, Ch. 47: *"When a person suppurates internally after pneumonia, fever is present together with a dry cough and difficulty in breathing; his feet swell, and the nails of both his hands and his feet become curved"* (Loeb, Vol. V, p271).

DISEASES II, Ch. 61: *"If dropsy arises in the lung, there are fever and coughing, and the patient respires rapidly; his feet swell, all his nails become curved, and he suffers the same things as a person that is suppurating internally, only more mildly and over a longer time"* (Loeb, Vol. V, p307).

The aura of epilepsy

The aura, the premonition that some epileptic patients have before the onset of a fit, and the unfortunate shame felt by some epileptics, is well described:

THE SACRED DISEASE, Ch. XV: *"Such as are habituated to their disease have a presentiment when an attack is imminent, and run away from men, home, if their house be near, if not, to the most deserted spot, where the fewest people will see the fall, and immediately hide their heads. This is the result of shame at their malady, and not, as the many hold, of fear of the divine"* (Loeb, Vol. II, p171).

Chapter 7

Hippocratic approaches to therapy

In the virtual absence of effective drugs, and without any real understanding of their patients' illnesses, it is interesting to observe how the Hippocratic doctors coped with therapy. Their treatments are summarized and categorized in Table 3.

The treatment of fractures and dislocations will be covered in Chapter 8. There is little doubt that, even by modern standards, a skilled Hippocratic doctor generally provided effective treatment in this area. I have also singled out the drainage of abscesses as a separate category in Table 3 since, unlike many other forms of therapy, it would have been of major direct benefit to the patient. However, the mainstay of Hippocratic therapy, and indeed of the maintenance of health in well people, seems to have been regimen i.e. diet and exercise, supplemented by purges of various sorts.

Hippocratic doctors regarded their role as one of assisting the body's normal healing processes. This is expressed very beautifully in the following piece:

EPIDEMICS VI, Section 5, Ch. 1: *"The body's nature is the physician in disease. Nature finds the way for herself, not from thought . . . Well trained, readily and without instruction, nature does what is needed"* (Loeb, Vol. VII, p255).

This presents the romantic view that 'Nature heals'. Of course, Nature does not always do what is needed to cure the patient. However, the idea of working with the body's natural processes to obtain healing was, and is, both interesting and valuable.

TABLE 3. Hippocratic methods of therapy

General
- regimen (diet and exercise)
- purges (emetics and enemas)
- venesection
- baths and fomentations
- cautery
- psychological

Drainage of abscesses

Treatment of fractures and dislocations

An interesting general point is that paternalistic attitudes on the part of doctors might not have been acceptable. Certainly, the opening lines of Affections suggest that patients expected to understand what was being done to them. Modern trends in this direction might therefore be going back full circle to Hippocratic times:

> AFFECTIONS, Ch. 1: *"Any man who is intelligent must, on considering that health is of the utmost value to human beings, have the personal understanding necessary to help himself in diseases, and be able to understand and to judge what physicians might say and what they administer to his body, being versed in each of these matters to a degree reasonable for a layman"* (Loeb, Vol. V, p7).

An ancient call for evidence-based medicine

A surprisingly large number of modern medical treatments are based merely on impressions or on inadequate clinical trials. Even senior Consultants within a specialty will sometimes have widely divergent views on how to approach a particular clinical problem. 'Evidence-based medicine' is a modern term which denotes a careful and systematic evaluation of individual therapies. This is done in order to ensure that resources are not wasted on ineffective treatments and—just as importantly—to ensure that effective therapies are identified and focused on the correct group of patients.

The author of Regimen in Acute Diseases clearly recognized the importance of this a long time ago, and we could not put it better today:

> REGIMEN IN ACUTE DISEASES, Ch. VII: *"And it seems to me worthwhile to write on such matters as are not yet ascertained by physicians, though knowledge thereof is important, and on them depend great benefit or great harm. For instance, it has not been ascertained why in acute diseases some physicians think that the correct treatment is to give unstrained barley-gruel throughout the illness; while others consider it to be of first-rate importance for the patient to swallow no particle of barley, holding that to do so is very harmful, but strain the juice through a cloth before they give it"* (Loeb, Vol. II, pp67,69).

Regimen and purges

There would have been excellent scope for giving sick patients a light diet (for example barley extracts and mixtures of honey with water) to maintain strength during the worst phases of their illness. Whatever the actual rationale, this would in practice help to sustain the patient long enough to allow normal body mechanisms to overcome the disease. However, diet, exercise and purging became extremely complicated ways not only of treating disease, but also of maintaining health.

An interesting point to note is that, even in ancient times, people were experimenting with diet to improve athletic performance:

ANCIENT MEDICINE, Ch. IV: *"At any rate even at the present day those who study gymnastics and athletic exercises are constantly making some fresh discovery by investigating on the same method what food and what drink are best assimilated and make a man grow stronger"* (Loeb, Vol. I, p21).

Moreover, correct regimen was reckoned to improve intelligence:

REGIMEN I, Ch. XXXV: *"But such souls are fairly constant in their attention, and this kind of man under right regimen may become more intelligent and sharper than natural endowment warrants. Such a one is benefited by using a regimen inclining rather towards fire, with no surfeit either of foods or of drinks. So he should take sharp runs, so that the body may be emptied of moisture and the moisture may be stayed sooner"* (Loeb, Vol. IV, pp283,285).

A whole treatise (Regimen in Health) is devoted to extraordinarily complicated advice on diet, together with the regular use of emetics and colonic irrigation, to maintain health. Clearly, food faddism has a long history, and the colonic irrigators of today can trace their ideas back to Hippocratic times. Here are some of the thoughts of the author of Regimen in Health:

REGIMEN IN HEALTH, Ch. I: *"The layman ought to order his regimen in the following way. In winter eat as much as possible and drink as little as possible; drink should be wine as undiluted as possible, and food should be bread, with all meats roasted; during this season take as few vegetables as possible, for so will the body be most dry and hot. When spring comes, increase drink and take it very diluted, taking a little at a time; use softer foods and less in quantity; substitute for bread barley-cake; on the same principle diminish meats, taking them all boiled instead of roasted, and eating when spring comes a few vegetables, in order that a man may be prepared for summer by taking all foods soft, meats boiled, and vegetables raw or boiled. Drinks should be as diluted and as copious as possible, the change to be slight, gradual and not sudden. In summer the barley-cake to be soft, the drink diluted and copious, and the meats in all cases boiled. For one must use these, when it is summer, that the body may become cold and soft. For the season is hot and dry, and makes bodies burning and parched. Accordingly these conditions must be counteracted by way of living"* (Loeb, Vol. IV, p45,47).

REGIMEN IN HEALTH, Ch V: *"Emetics and clysters for the bowels should be used thus. Use emetics during the six winter months, for this period engenders more phlegm than does the summer, and in it occur the diseases that attack the head and the region above the diaphragm. But when the weather is hot use clysters, for the season is burning, the body bilious, heaviness is felt in the loins and knees, feverishness comes on and colic in the belly. So the body must be cooled, and the humours that rise must be drawn downwards from these regions. For people inclined to fatness and moistness let the clysters be rather salt and thin; for those inclined to dryness, leanness and weakness let them be rather greasy and thick. Greasy, thick clysters are prepared from milk, or water boiled with chick-peas or similar things. Thin, salt clysters are made of things like brine and sea-water. Emetics should be employed thus. Men who are fat and not thin should take an emetic fasting after running or walking quickly in the middle of the day. Let the emetic consist of half a cotyle* of hyssop compounded with a chous† of water, and let the patient drink this, pouring in vinegar and adding salt, in such a way as to make the mixture as agreeable as possible. Let him drink it quietly at first, and then more quickly"* (Loeb, Vol. IV, p51).

Most extreme of all is the advice given by the author of Regimen III, who suggests that those who can afford it should devote their entire lives to the maintenance of their health! It reminded me of the beautiful parody of the mindless pursuit of 'perfect' health entitled 'The Last Well Person'[12]. The flamboyant and boastful personality of the author of Regimen III comes out strongly. It contrasts starkly with the measured, publicity-shunning character of the author of On Joints and On Fractures:

REGIMEN III, Ch. LXIX: *"Such is my advice to the great mass of mankind, who of necessity live a haphazard life without the chance of neglecting everything to concentrate on taking care of their health. But when a man is thus favourably situated, and is convinced that neither wealth nor anything else is of any value without health, I can add to his blessings a regimen that I have discovered, one that approximates to the truth as closely as is possible. What it is I will set forth in the sequel. This discovery reflects glory on myself its discoverer, and is useful to those who have learnt it, but no one of my predecessors has even attempted to understand it, though I judge it to be of great value in respect of everything else. It comprises prognosis before illness and diagnosis of what is the matter with the body, whether food overpowers exercise, whether exercise overpowers food, or whether*

---

*Approximately 150 ml.
†Approximately 3.5 litres.

the two are duly proportioned. For it is from the overpowering of one or the other that diseases arise, while from their being evenly balanced comes good health" (Loeb, Vol. IV, pp381,383).

Various medications were used to induce vomiting, especially the poisonous hellebore (presumably one of the *Helleborus* species) and the more pleasant hyssop (presumably *Hyssopus officinalis*). However, a wide variety of extraordinary concoctions were described as emetics and enemas. Here are three examples:

INTERNAL AFFECTIONS, Ch. 26: *"Administer this other enema in whichever disease you wish: take two cotylai* of white wine, a half-cotyle each of honey and oil, and a fourth-cotyle of burnt Egyptian soda, and cut off the leaves of a squirting-cucumber plant and squeeze out a cotyle of juice; mix all these ingredients together, pour them into a small pot, and then boil and administer as an enema"* (Loeb, Vol. VI, pp163,165).

INTERNAL AFFECTIONS, Ch. 51: *"If this does not help, you must clean him with the following enema: grind a half-cotyle of cummin, bray an uncut bottle-gourd of the small round kind in a mortar, sift the fourth part of a mina of red Egyptian soda as fine as possible, roast, grind fine, mix these together, and pour into a pot; add a cotyle of oil, a half-cotyle of honey, a cotyle of sweet white wine, and two cotylai of beets; boil these until you think they have the proper consistency; then strain through a linen cloth, and add a cotyle of Attic honey to them, if you do not wish to boil the honey together with them; if you do not have Attic honey, mix in a cotyle of the best kind you have, and boil in a mortar; if the fluid is too thick, pour in some of the same wine, judging according to the thickness; administer as an enema"* (Loeb, Vol. VI, pp245,247).

INTERNAL AFFECTIONS, Ch. 27: *"If choking comes on, you must give the following medication until the patient vomits: honey and water, vinegar and salt; mix these together and pour them into a new pot; then warm, and add twigs of the head-shaped marjoram with their seeds; when it is warm give to the patient to drink off; then cover him with blankets, wrapping him so that he will sweat heavily, and leave him. When vomiting occurs, let him vomit actively by being tickled with a feather. If vomiting does not occur, make the patient provoke it by drinking, in addition, a two-cotyle cup of warm melicrat†"* (Loeb, Vol. VI, p169).

There are long and detailed descriptions of many foods in Regimen II, especially in relation to their warmth, dryness, heat and moisture.

---

*A cotyle is approximately 300 ml.
†Honey and water mixture.

One has to remember that the Hippocratic doctor gave food to correct perceived imbalances of these properties in the body. Here are three examples:

REGIMEN II, Ch. XLVII: *"With birds it is as follows. All birds almost are drier than beasts, for those creatures which have no bladder neither make urine nor have spittle, by reason of the heat of the belly. For the moisture of the body is consumed to nourish the heat; wherefore they neither urinate nor spit. Therefore that which wants such moisture must necessarily be dry. The flesh of ringdoves is the driest, secondly partridges, thirdly pigeons, cocks and turtles. The flesh of geese is the most moist. Those which feed on seed are drier than the others. Ducks and fowls that feed on marshes or waters are all moist"* (Loeb, Vol. IV, pp319,320).

REGIMEN II, Ch. XLVIII: *"As to the flesh of fish, these are the driest. The scorpion fish, dragon fish, the fish called callionymos, the piper, the grey fish, the perch, the fish called thrissa. The fish that frequent stony places are almost all light, as the thrush fish, the hake, the gudgeon and elephitis. These are lighter than those which move from place to place, for these remaining quiet have a rare and light flesh, but those which wander and are wave-tossed have a more solid and deeper flesh, being much battered by the toil. The torpedo, skate, turbot and such-like are light. All those fish that feed in muddy and marshy places, as mullet, cestreus, eels and the like are heavier (of digestion), because they feed upon muddy water and other things which grow therein"* (Loeb, Vol. IV, p321).

REGIMEN II, Ch. XLV: *"Lentils are heating and trouble the bowels; they are neither laxative nor astringent. Bitter vetches are binding, strengthening, fattening, filling, and give a person a good colour. Linseed is nourishing, astringent, and somewhat refreshing. Clary seed is much of the same nature as linseed. Lupins are in their nature strengthening and heating, but by preparation they become more light and cooling than they are naturally, and pass by stool. Hedge-mustard seed moistens and passes by stool"* (Loeb, Vol. IV, p317).

Diet and exercise were used as a form of therapy throughout the treatises, even as an adjunct to the setting of fractures. In some situations, the dietary recommendations would have sustained the patient, and been of benefit. However, the whole area became immensely and unnecessarily complicated. Here are two extreme examples. For a patient with a disease described as ileus (although the description does not resemble the condition covered by that name in modern medicine):

INTERNAL AFFECTIONS, Ch. 44: *"On the following day, twice give a chous* of boiled ass's milk with salt, for the patient to drink off, and towards evening have him eat for dinner bread and, as main dish, boiled mutton and polyp boiled in dark wine, and drink the sauce too; also let him have lentil-soup prepared thus: boil a cotyle† of lentils and mash them fine; then mix in meal, shred in silphium, and add salt; add vinegar, and boil in garlic; over this pour water, bring to a boil two or three times, and stir together; then let the patient take this and eat it as a main dish; it should not be too thick; also add boiled penny-royal, for the aroma. On the days between medications, let the patient induce vomiting every sixth day"* (Loeb, Vol. VI, pp221,223).

For consumption:

INTERNAL AFFECTIONS, Ch. 12: *"...first administer a vapour-bath; on that day after the patient has had the vapour-bath, give him a half chous‡ of melicrat to which a little vinegar has been added; have him drink this off without taking a breath, and then cover him thickly with blankets, and leave these on for a good long time. If he cannot tolerate this, but wants to vomit, let him vomit. If vomiting does not occur after a certain time has elapsed, let the patient drink, in addition, a large cup of warm water, and vomit by being tickled with a feather. When he has vomited, and feels better, let him rest that day. When dinner time arrives, have him dine on a small barley-cake, and take as main dish salt-fish and leeks, of which he should eat as many as he can; let his wine be sweet. From then on, let the patient bathe every day at dawn in very copious hot water; after the bath, you must make sure that he does not have a chill, by putting him to bed, and having him sleep long. On arising from his sleep, have him walk at least twenty stades§ that day; on the days that follow, let him walk an additional five stades each day until he reaches one hundred stades"* (Loeb, Vol. VI, pp109,111).

---

*Approximately 3.5 litres (!)
†Approximately 300 ml
‡Approximately 1.8 litres
§Approximately 4 kilometres

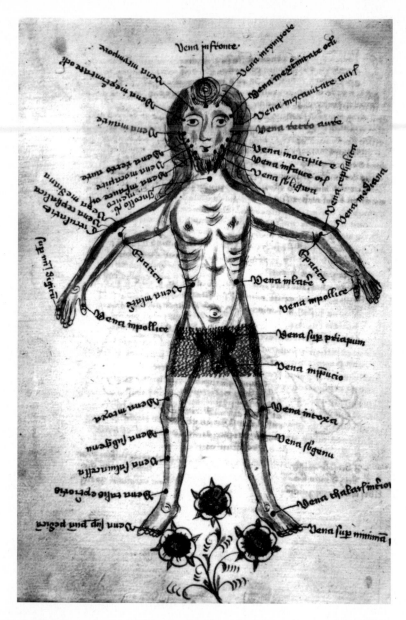

Figure 3. Phlebotomy chart-mannikin showing the various places for venesection. 15th century MS. in the Royal Library, Dresden. Reprinted with the kind permission of the Wellcome Institute Library, London.

Venesection

The use of venesection varies considerably among different treatises. Although the rationale for its use is not clear, it might have been intended to reduce heat in the body, as blood was considered to have much heat. This is suggested by the following:

DISEASES III, Ch. 14: *"Treat this patient as follows: clean out his upper cavity as quickly as possible, draw blood from his head and the bends of his arms, in order to remove the overheating of the upper cavity, and cool the region above the diaphragm, except for the heart"* (Loeb, Vol. VI, p29).

Figure 4. Therapeutics: Blood-letting. Woman performing cupping upon another, after a bath. 15th century German wood-cut from 'Kalender', 1483. Reprinted with the kind permission of the Wellcome Institute Library, London.

It is interesting to note the importance given to the site from which the blood was taken, as alluded to in the preceding quotation, a concept carried forward into modern times (Figure 3). As Hippocratic doctors were unaware of the circulation of the blood, they probably thought that venesection would influence mainly the part from which the blood was taken. Here is another example:

EPIDEMICS II, SECTION 4, Ch. 5: *"The house servant of Stymarges, who did not even bleed when she bore a daughter, had the mouth of her womb retroverted. She had pain in her hip joint and leg. Phlebotomy at the ankle relieved her"* (Loeb, Vol. VII, p73).

Venesection (Figure 4) would rarely have been of benefit to the patient, and might often have been harmful, given the scale of blood-letting suggested in some parts of the Corpus. Here are two extreme examples:

EPIDEMICS V, Ch. 6: *"In Oeniadae, a man was held by a disease...He wasted in body and grew thin, he got no nourishment from his food when he ate, and the food passed out useless and burned...He drank various drugs to purge upward and downward, and was not benefited. But when he was bled in each arm in turn until he was bloodless, then he was benefited and freed from the trouble"* (Loeb, Vol. VII, p157).

REGIMEN IN ACUTE DISEASES (APPENDIX), Ch. 31: *"If the pain radiates upwards to the collar-bone, or is located about the breast or in the arm, you must incise the inner vessel of the arm on the affected side as follows: draw off, according to the condition of the body, the season, and the patient's age and colour, a considerable amount, and even venture, if intense pain is present, to continue until the loss of consciousness; afterwards administer an enema"* (Loeb, Vol. VI, pp295,297).

Cautery

As has been described in preceding sections, cautery (Figures 5, 6) was used for pain relief, and for the incision of abscesses, especially deep abscesses. In other situations the rationale for its use is not clear. The author of Internal Affections seemed especially keen on the use of cautery, and here are two examples. In neither case would the patient have benefited from the cautery:

For a liver disease:

INTERNAL AFFECTIONS, Ch. 28: *"If the disease does not come to an end thus, you must cauterize, when the liver is largest and most protuberant, with boxwood spindles; dip these in boiling oil, and apply them until you think you have accomplished what you wanted and the cautery is adequate; or burn eight eschars with mushrooms. For, if your cautery succeeds, you will make the patient well, and he will pass the time from then on more easily. But if he is neither cauterized successfully nor brought to health by any of the other treatments, he wastes away after that, and in time dies"* (Loeb, Vol. VI, pp173,175).

For a kidney disease:

INTERNAL AFFECTIONS, Ch. 18: *"If the disease does not go away with this treatment, fatten the patient on milk, and burn four eschars beside his right shoulder-blade, three into the acetabulum of his right hip-joint, two under his buttock, two in the middle of his thigh, and one each above his knee and ankle. If a person is cauterized in this way, it will not allow the disease to migrate either upwards or downwards. If, however, pain breaks out first, and, before you can cauterize, it becomes fixed in the leg, the patient will become lame"* (Loeb, Vol. VI, p133).

Figure 5. A surgeon applying a cautery iron to clearly defined points on a woman's lower abdomen (indicating the liver?). Pen drawing after a tenth century manuscript. Reprinted with the kind permission of the Wellcome Institute Library, London.

Figure 6. A receptacle for burning coal to heat cautery instruments. Engraving. Reprinted with the kind permission of the Wellcome Institute Library, London.

Psychological aspects of therapy

One of the more interesting general points to note is that at least some ancient doctors were aware of the psychological aspects of therapy, i.e. the healing effect on some conditions of confidence and trust in one's doctor. This is described in modern medicine as the placebo effect. While it is obviously of critical importance to distinguish placebo effects from the fundamental biological effects of any new therapy in modern clinical trials, harnessing the powerful therapeutic effects of the mind for physical symptoms of psychological origin is a challenge that modern mainstream medicine has largely failed to grasp, but which alternative medicine has embraced enthusiastically. That it could be put to powerful use was well recognized by the author of Precepts:

PRECEPTS, Ch. VI: *"For some patients, though conscious that their condition is perilous, recover their health simply through their contentment with the goodness of the physician"* (Loeb, Vol. I, p319).

Drainage of abscesses

Pneumonias were frequent, and without antibiotics empyema would have been a common complication. Draining empyemas is described on several occasions. Here is the best example, with the description of an interesting physical sign for deciding on which side the pus is located (by listening for fluid movement of the associated effusion) and the use of a tin drainage tube. It is also worth pondering if the alcohol in the wine in the irrigation fluid might have had antimicrobial effects:

DISEASES II, Ch. 47: *"When the fifteenth day after the pus has broken out into the cavity arrives, wash this patient in copious hot water, and seat him on a chair that does not move; have some-one hold his arms, and you shake him by the shoulders, listening on which of his sides there is a sound; prefer to incise on the left side, for it is less dangerous. If, because of the thickness and abundance of pus, there is no sound for you to hear—for sometimes this happens—on whichever side there is swelling and more pain, make an incision as low down as possible, behind the swelling rather than in front of it, in order that the exit you make for the pus will allow freedom of flow. First cut the skin between the ribs with a bellied scalpel; then wrap a lancet with a piece of cloth, leaving the point of the blade exposed a length equal to the nail of your thumb, and insert it. When you have removed as much pus as you think appropriate, plug the wound with a tent of raw linen, and tie it with a cord; draw off pus once a day; on the tenth day, draw all the pus, and plug the wound with linen. Then make an infusion of warm wine and oil with a tube, in order that the lung, accustomed to being soaked in pus, will not be suddenly dried out; discharge the morning infusion towards evening, and the evening one in the morning. When the pus is thin like water, sticky when touched with a finger, and small in amount, insert a hollow tin drainage tube"* (Loeb, Vol. V, pp273,275).

The crucial importance of draining pus was well recognized. The author of Epidemics V felt that he might have saved the following patient had drainage been adequate:

EPIDEMICS V, Ch. 7: *"But the pains did not leave him: pus possessed the hip, and the perineum, and the groin area, all of which were even more painful. The pus was nearer the depth of the bone than of the flesh, and it was not obvious for a time that he was in that condition until he grew weak. Then he was cauterized. The scars were numerous, large, and close together. Much thick pus ran out. He died a few days after that, from the size and number of the wounds and from weakness of his body. It would appear that, if there had been a single incision adequate for drainage and the pus had been drawn toward the incision and, if another incision had been needed, one adequate for drainage had been cut: if this had been done to him at the right time, it seems that he would have become healthy"* (Loeb, Vol. VII, pp157,159).

The use of cautery to drain deep abscesses, and the risk of cutting vital structures was well recognized:

DISEASES I, Ch. 10: *"Dexterity is as follows: when a person is incising or cauterizing, that he does not cut a cord or vessel; if he is cauterizing a patient with internal suppuration, that he hits the pus, and when cutting, the same"* (Loeb, Vol. V, p121).

Analgesia

Pain relief appears not to have been an important consideration in the Hippocratic treatises. Presumably, in the absence of effective analgesia, the best thing to do was to plough on. That Hippocratic doctors probably worked with little or no effective analgesia is suggested by the following piece. Clearly, the doctor was able to minimize pain only by a thoughtful planning of his procedures:

PHYSICIAN, Ch. 5: *"In surgical operations that consist in incising or cautery, speed or slowness are commended alike, for each has its value. In cases where the surgery is performed by a single incision, you must make it a quick one; for since the person being cut generally suffers pain, this suffering should last for the least time possible, and that will be achieved if the incision is made quickly. However, when many incisions are necessary, you must employ a slow surgery, for a surgeon that was fast would make the pain sustained and great, whereas intervals provide a break in its intensity for the patients"* (Loeb, Vol. VIII, p307).

An apparently obvious possibility, the use of alcohol, is not mentioned. Another possibility, the use of opium, also goes unmentioned, although opium was well known in ancient Egypt. Perhaps the psychological effects of opium were known, but its analgesic properties were not. There is a mention of the poppy plant in Internal Affections, but in relation to dietary treatment of a 'typhus', not in the context of analgesia:

INTERNAL AFFECTIONS, Ch. 40: *"Boil ten grains of peony seed in dark wine, and give to drink; boil turnips well, and have the patient drink their juice, after seasoning it with unsalted cheese, poppy, oil, salt, silphium and vinegar"* (Loeb, Vol. VI, p207).

Potions prepared specifically for pain relief are mentioned on a couple of occasions, but it is unlikely that they would have been effective. For patients with a hepatic disorder the following drink is recommended:

INTERNAL AFFECTIONS, Ch. 27: *"Against the pain you must give the following to drink: mash the yolk of a boiled hen's egg, pour in a half-cotyle* of nightshade juice, and add a quarter-cotyle of melicrat made with water; mix these together and give to the patient to drink; you will stop the pain; give this each day until the pain ceases"* (Loeb, Vol. VI, p167).

It is difficult to relate modern botanical nomenclature to that of the ancient Greeks, but some species of the Nightshade family are extremely poisonous, and one can only guess that the nightshade alluded to here is not Deadly Nightshade (*Atropa belladonna*). Atropine is the well known drug found in Deadly Nightshade. It is possible that related alkaloids with analgesic properties are found in other members of the Nightshade family. However, it is more likely that the side-effects of the potion distracted the patient's attention from the pain, or that it functioned as a placebo. Here is an ointment for pain relief:

REGIMEN IN ACUTE DISEASES (APPENDIX), Ch. 67: *"Against sharp pains and fluxes: let there be a drachma[†] of copper ore, and grapes; when this has fermented for two days, press it out, knead into it myrrh and saffron, and add new wine; heat in the sun, and with this anoint persons suffering from sharp pains; let it be kept in a copper vessel"* (Loeb, Vol. VI, pp325,327).

*Approximately 150 ml
†Approximately 5 grammes

The application of warmth to painful areas is mentioned on several occasions, and would have been effective to some degree, as we all know from personal experience:

REGIMEN IN ACUTE DISEASES, Ch XXI: *"When there is pain in the side, whether at the beginning or later, it is not amiss to try to dissipate it first by hot fomentations. The best fomentation is hot water in a skin, or bladder, or bronze or earthen vessel. Apply something soft to the side first to prevent discomfort. A good thing also to apply is a big, soft sponge dipped in hot water and squeezed out. You must, however, cover up the heat on the upper part, for doing so will make it hold out and last for a longer time; besides, it will prevent the steam being carried towards the breath of the patient—unless indeed the patient's breathing it be considered an advantage, as in fact it occasionally is"* (Loeb, Vol. II, pp79,80).

Cautery of the skin is occasionally recommended for pain relief. Of course, it would achieve nothing other than to distract the patient from the original pain by perhaps a greater pain!

Chapter 8

Fractures, dislocations and other injuries

The three long treatises dealing with trauma (On Wounds in the Head, On Fractures, On Joints) are the most accessible of the medical treatises of the Corpus to the modern reader for reasons discussed in the introduction to Chapter 5. They are also among the best written, by an authoritative author (or authors) with a wealth of clinical experience. It is clear that the treatment offered in this area by good Hippocratic doctors was excellent.

An interesting thing about these three treatises is that nowhere could I see any mention of analgesia. Analgesia does not, in fact, figure strongly in the Corpus as a whole. In any case, the absence of pain relief would have made the reduction of fractures and dislocations excruciatingly painful procedures.

Fractures

The reduction of some fractures, especially of the leg, would have required considerable force. Various mechanical contraptions were therefore devised, as in the following case for fractures or dislocations at the ankle:

ON FRACTURES, Ch. XIII: *"As a rule two men suffice, one pulling one way and one the other, but if they cannot do it, it is easy to make the extension more powerful. Thus, one should fix a wheel-nave or something similar in the ground, put a soft wrapping round the foot, and then binding broad straps of ox-hide about it attach the ends of the straps to a pestle or some other rod. Put the end of the rod into the wheel-nave and pull back, while assistants hold the patient on the upper side grasping both at the shoulders and hollow of the knee"* (Loeb, Vol. III, pp127,129).

The most famous device was the 'Hippocratic bench'. It has been interpreted in various ways from the following detailed description, which is best read while referring to the diagram of Littré (the famous 19th Century French translator of the Corpus) in Figure 7:

ON JOINTS, Ch. LXXII *"It was said before that it is worth while for one who practises in a populous city to get a quadrangular plank, six cubits* long or rather more, and about two cubits*

*6 cubits is approximately 10 feet or 3 metres

51

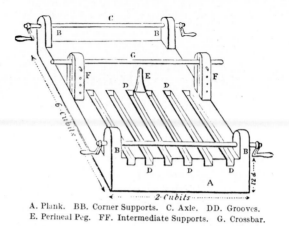

A. Plank.   BB. Corner Supports.   C. Axle.   DD. Grooves.
E. Perineal Peg.   FF. Intermediate Supports.   G. Crossbar.

Figure 7. The Hippocratic bench, according to the 19th century French translator of the Corpus, Littré. Reprinted with the kind permission of Harvard University Press.

broad; while for thickness a span is sufficient. Next, it should have an incision at either end of the long sides, that the mechanism may not be higher than is suitable. Then let there be short strong supports, firmly fitted in, and having a windlass at each end. It suffices, next, to cut out five or six long grooves about four fingers' breadth apart; it will be enough if they are three fingers broad and the same in depth, occupying half the plank, though there is no objection to their extending the whole length. The plank should also have a deeper hole cut out in the middle, about three fingers' breadth square; and into this hole insert, when requisite, a post, fitted to it, but rounded in the upper part. Insert it, whenever it seems useful, between the perineum and the head of the thigh-bone. This post, when fixed, prevents the body from yielding when traction is made towards the feet; in fact, sometimes the post of itself is a substitute for counter-extension upwards. Some times also, when the leg is extended in both directions, this same post, so placed as to have free play to either side, would be suitable for levering the head of the thigh-bone outwards. It is for this purpose, too, that the grooves are cut, that a wooden lever may be inserted into whichever may suit, and brought to bear either at the side of the joint-heads or right upon them, making pressure simultaneously with the extension, whether the leverage is required outwards or inwards, and whether the lever should be rounded or broad, for one form suits one joint, another another. This leverage, combined with extension, is very efficacious in all reductions of the leg-joints." (Loeb, Vol. III, p373, 375).

The reduction of a fractured tibia and fibula is typical of the descriptions of several reductions:

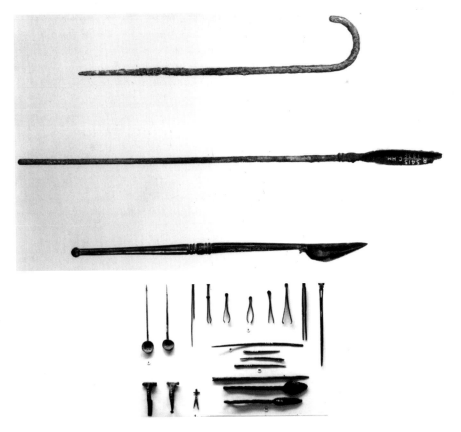

Figure 8. Greek and Roman surgical instruments.
Top: Cryptotome, found when dragging the Tiber at Rome. A gouge and curette, both found near the Temple of Bacchus at Pereia, Greece.
Bottom: set of instruments found at Peronne, Somme.
Reprinted with the kind permission of the Wellcome Institute Library, London.

ON FRACTURES, Ch. XV: *"When both leg-bones are broken without an external wound, stronger* extension is required. If there is much overlapping make extension by some of those methods which have been described. But extensions made by man-power are also sufficient, for in most cases two strong men are enough, one pulling at each end. The traction should be in a straight line in accordance with the natural direction of the leg and thigh, both when it is being made for fractures of the leg bones and of the thigh"* (Loeb, Vol. III, pp133,135).

For difficult compound fractures, levers were used to re-align the broken bones (Figure 8):

*Stronger than in the case of broken arm bones

ON FRACTURES, Ch. XXXI: *"In cases where the fractured and projecting bones cannot be settled into their proper place, the following is the method of reduction. One must have iron rods made in fashion like the levers used by stone masons, broader at one end and narrower at the other. There should be three and even more that one may use those most suitable. Then one should use these, while extension is going on, to make leverage, pressing the under side of the iron on the lower bone, and the upper side against the upper bone, in a word just as if one would lever up violently a stone or log"* (Loeb, Vol. III, pp171,173).

Once appropriate extension had been obtained and the broken bones realigned, a complex series of bandages was put in place to help maintain the bones in proper alignment. The bandages were changed periodically, presumably to cope with the varying degrees of swelling, and splints were applied after a week or so, as described here for a broken humerus:

ON FRACTURES, Ch. VIII: *"Then let him do the bandaging, putting the heads of the bandages on the fracture and performing all the rest of the operation as previously directed. Let him ask the same questions, and use the same indications to judge whether things are right or not. He should bandage every third day and use greater pressure, and on the seventh or ninth day put it up in splints. If he suspects the bone is not in good position, let him loosen the dressings towards the middle of this period, and after putting it right, re-apply them.*

The bone of the upper arm usually consolidates in forty days. When these are passed one should undo the dressings and diminish the pressure and the number of bandages" (Loeb, Vol. III, p117).

The treatment of crush fractures of the vertebral bodies would have been a particularly difficult problem:

ON JOINTS, Ch. XLII: *"When the hump-back* is due to a fall, attempts at straightening rarely succeed. For, to begin with, succussions on a ladder never straightened any case, so far as I know, and the practitioners who use this method are chiefly those who want to make the vulgar herd gape, for to such it seems marvellous to see a man suspended or shaken or treated in such ways; and they always applaud these performances, never troubling themselves about the result of the operation, whether bad or good. As to the practitioners who devote themselves to this kind of thing, those at least whom I have known are incompetent."* (Loeb, Vol. III, pp283, 285).

*Unusually pronounced curvature of the vertebral column, consequent on crush fractures of the vertebral bodies

This method of treatment, although roundly condemned, was illustrated in a 9th century commentary on the Corpus (Figure 9). An alternative, but equally ineffective approach using a variant of the Hippocratic bench, is illustrated in Figure 10.

The importance of elevation to reduce swelling seems to have been well appreciated. In the case of fractures of the ankle, the following advice is given:

ON FRACTURES, Ch. XI: *"One must see that the foot is, as a rule, a little higher than the rest of the body"* (Loeb, Vol. III, p127).

Figure 9. Reducing a dislocated spine. From a ninth century Greek manuscript in the Laurentian Library, Florence. A commentary by Apollonius of Kitium on the Hippocratic treatise On Dislocation. Reprinted with the kind permission of the Wellcome Institute Library, London.

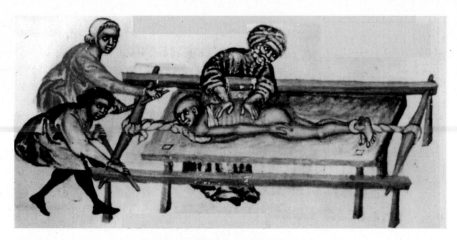

Figure 10. Reduction, in the Moslem Middle Ages, by hand pressure. From a 14th century Latin translation of Albucasis' surgery; Vienna, NB, MS. 2641, fol. 76v. Reprinted with the kind permission of the Wellcome Institute Library, London.

The problem of disuse causing atrophy was also known:
> IN THE SURGERY, Ch. XX: *"(Remember) that use strengthens, disuse debilitates"* (Loeb, Vol. III, p77).

Dislocations

A dislocation of the hip joint would require considerable force to relocate the head of the femur in the acetabulum. For the Hippocratic doctor it required a heroic and (to the modern eye) faintly farcical procedure:
> ON FRACTURES, Ch. LXX: *"Dislocation of the thigh at the hip should be reduced as follows, if it is dislocated inwards. It is a good and correct method, and in accord with nature, and one too that has something striking about it, which pleases a dilettante in such matters. One should suspend the patient by his feet from a cross-beam with a band, strong, but soft, and of good breadth. The feet should be about four fingers apart, or even less. He should also be bound round above the knee-caps with a broad, soft band stretching up to the beam; and the injured leg should be extended about two fingers' breadth further than the other. Let the head be about two cubits*, more or less, from the ground. The patient should have his arms extended along the sides and fastened with something soft. Let all these preparations be made while he is lying on his back, that the period of suspension may be as short as possible. When he is suspended, let an assistant who is skilful and no weakling insert his forearm between the patient's thighs, and bring it down between the perineum and the head of*

*Approximately 1 metre

the dislocated bone. Thus, clasping the inserted hand with the other, while standing erect beside the suspended patient, let him suddenly suspend himself from him, and keep himself in the air as evenly balanced as possible. This mode of reduction provides everything requisite according to nature, for the body itself when suspended makes extension by its own weight; the assistant who is suspended, while making suspension, forces the head of the bone to a position above the socket, and at the same time levers it out with the bone of his forearm, and makes it slip into its old natural place. But the bandages must be perfectly arranged, and care taken that the suspended assistant is the strongest available" (Loeb, Vol. III, pp367,369).

The shoulder joint is fairly easily dislocated, and recurrent dislocations can be annoying and difficult to treat, even in modern times. It is interesting to note that the major problems cited for this disability in Classical Greece were in gymnastics and warfare:
ON JOINTS, Ch. XI: *"The proper treatment of those whose shoulders are often being dislocated is a thing worth learning. For many have been debarred from gymnastic contests, though well fitted in all other respects, and many have become worthless in warfare and have perished through this misfortune. Another reason for its importance is the fact that I know of no one who uses the correct treatment, some not even attempting to take it in hand, while others have theories and practices the reverse of what is appropriate"* (Loeb, Vol. III, p223).

The treatment was fairly drastic, and presumably aimed to create scar tissue in the armpit to try to hold the joint in place:
ON JOINTS, Ch. XI: *"One should cauterize these cases thus:- Grasp the skin at the armpit between the fingers and draw it in the direction towards which the head of the humerus gets dislocated (i.e. downwards), then pass the cautery right through the skin thus drawn away. The cautery irons for this operation should not be thick nor very rounded, but elongated (for so they pass through more quickly), and pressure should be made with the hand. They should be white hot, so that the operation may be completed with all possible speed"* (Loeb, Vol. III, p225).

Head wounds

Although the general philosophy of the Corpus tends to non-intervention unless necessary, in the case of head injuries, early trephining was prescribed in most instances. ET Withington summarized the Hippocratic position well: "an injured skull should have a hole made in it if there is not one already" (Loeb, Vol. III, page

3). The therapeutic benefit might have been to reduce intracranial pressure by allowing room for expansion of the brain when haemorrhage or oedema was present. However, the risk of serious infection would have been great, especially if the dura mater was pierced.

Trephination, for medical or superstitious reasons, long pre-dated Greek medicine (Figure 11). It is interesting to note that the enthusiasm for trephining (presumably with a cylindrical saw) quickly waned in classical Greece, even though it carried the authority of Hippocrates[11]. Nevertheless, it was practised in medieval and later times (Figure 12).

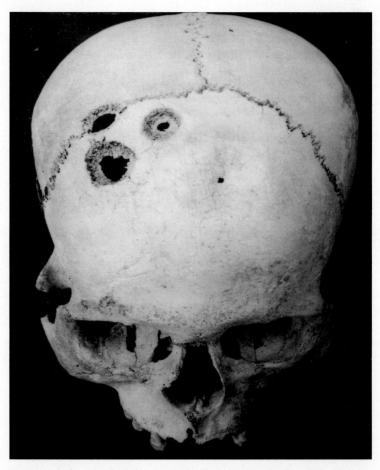

Figure 11. Prehistoric trephination. A skull excavated at Jericho, 1958 showing three trephinations, two of which show healing. Reprinted with the kind permission of the Wellcome Institute Library, London.

Figure 12. Trephination: 13th century. Trephination of the skull in the Middle-Ages by means of the primitive throng drill. Source: Laudian Miscellany, 13th century MS. No. 724, Bodleian Library, Oxford. Reprinted with the kind permission of the Wellcome Institute Library, London.

There follows a typical case history. The young girl's general condition is not clear, but one can't help thinking that the trephining, if anything, hastened her demise:

EPIDEMICS V, Ch. 28: *"At Omilus, a young girl of about twelve years died in midsummer from a wound in the head, on the fourteenth day. Someone hit her with a door and crushed and shattered her skull. The sutures were in the wound. This was recognized properly as needing trephination. It was trephined, but not sufficiently. As some bone was left, pus developed there. On the eighth day shivering and fever seized her. When free from fever she was not as she should have been, but was as on the previous days. On the ninth day the rest was trephined, and a little pus with blood appeared. The membrane was clean. Sleep seized her, but the fever did not go away again. Spasms seized her left hand, since the wound was on the right"* (Loeb, Vol. VII, pp179,181).

The method of trephining is given as follows, the "membrane" referred to being the dura mater

ON WOUNDS IN THE HEAD, Ch. XXI: *"As to trephining when it is necessary to trephine a patient, keep the following in mind. If you operate after taking on the treatment from the beginning, you should not, in trephining, remove the bone at once down to the membrane, for it is not good for the membrane to be denuded of bone and exposed to morbid influences for a long time, or it may end by becoming macerated. There is also another danger that, if you immediately remove the bone by trephining down to the membrane, you may, in operating, wound the membrane with the trephine. You should rather stop the operation when there is very little left to be sawn through, and the bone is movable; and allow it to separate of its own accord"* (Loeb, Vol. III, p47).

Neurological injuries

It is interesting to note that the Hippocratic doctors were aware that lesions to one side of the brain affected the opposite side of the body. This is mentioned in the preceding case history of the young girl with the head injury, and is stated clearly in the following piece:

ON WOUNDS IN THE HEAD, Ch. XIX: *"Most cases have spasm of the parts on one side of the body; if the patient has the lesion on the left side of the head, spasm seizes the right side of the body; if he has the lesion on the right side of the head, spasm seizes the left side of the body"* (Loeb, Vol. III, p45).

They were also aware of the severe complications of spinal cord injuries:

PRORRHETIC II, Ch. 16: *"If the spinal marrow ails either as the result of a fall or some other manifest cause, or spontaneously, the person loses the power over his legs, so that on being touched he does not perceive it, and over his belly and bladder, so that in the early days of the disease he passes neither stool nor urine, unless forced. As the disease becomes older, stool and urine pass without the person's perceiving it; he dies not very long after that"* (Loeb, Vol. VIII, pp257,259).

Tendon injuries

The problem of imbalance of muscle tone following tendon injuries, although obviously not understood, was precisely noted:

EPIDEMICS 4, Ch. 60: *"That tendons draw towards themselves the following is indication: if the tendons on top of the hand be wounded the hand nods down, drawn by the tendons below. And vice versa"* (Loeb, Vol. VII, p151).

Military medicine

There is relatively little said about military medicine in the Corpus. However, it seems to have been the practice for doctors to accompany military expeditions, as suggested by the following:

PHYSICIAN, Ch. 14: *"Related to this is the surgery of wounds arising in military service, which concerns the extraction of missiles. In city practice experience of these is but little, for very rarely even in a whole lifetime are there civil or military combats. In fact such things occur most frequently and continuously in armies abroad. Thus, the person intending to practice this kind of surgery must serve in the army, and accompany it on expeditions abroad; for in this way he would become experienced in this practice"* (Loeb, Vol. VIII, p315).

Here are two case histories of soldiers hit by arrows:

EPIDEMICS V, Ch. 46: *"The man hit by an arrow in the gland at the groin, whom we had seen, was preserved in a most unexpected manner. The point was not removed because it was in too deep, nor was there any notable hemorrhage, nor inflammation, nor was he lamed. He had carried the point for six years up to the time of our departure. The suspicion was that the point was buried beneath in the midst of his tendons, and that no vein and artery were lacerated"* (Loeb, Vol. VII, pp187,189).

EPIDEMICS V, Ch. 98: *"Aristippus was severely wounded by being shot in the upper belly by an arrow. Terrible pain in the intestine. It was quickly inflamed, but no excrement passed below. He was nauseous; very bilious matter; when he had vomited he seemed better, but shortly later had the terrible pains again. His intestine as in intestinal obstructions. Fever, thirst. He died in seven days"* (Loeb, Vol. VII, p215).

An interesting general point is that there is virtually no mention of suturing in the treatises. Perhaps apposition of the cut edges of skin was effected by bandaging. This would have given better drainage of the wound, probably an important factor before antisepsis and antibiotics. Perhaps suturing was left to those "skilled in the use of the knife" (cf The Oath), an occupation considered unsuitable for doctors of the time. Here is one mention of suturing, following the cutting of the nostril to allow cautery of nasal polyps:

DISEASES II, Ch. 36: *"Another polyp: from inside near the cartilage for some reason a hardness forms; it appears to be flesh but, if you touch it, it makes a sound like stone. When the case is such, divide the nostril with a scalpel, clean the polyp out, and then apply cautery. After you do this, stitch the nostril together, and heal the ulcer by anointing it with ointment"* (Loeb, Vol. V, p251).

Chapter 9

Dreams, haemorrhoids and other miscellaneous points

Several interesting insights into the life and times of the Hippocratic doctor cannot comfortably be accommodated under the previous headings, but should not go unstated; hence this section.

Dreams

One of the most charming and prescient descriptions in the Corpus was, for me, that of dreams by the author of Regimen IV, thus:

REGIMEN IV, Ch. LXXXVI: *"He who has learnt aright about the signs that come in sleep will find that they have an important influence upon all things. For when the body is awake the soul is its servant, and is never her own mistress, but divides her attention among many things, assigning a part of it to each faculty of the body—to hearing, to sight, to touch, to walking, and to acts of the whole body; but the mind never enjoys independence. But when the body is at rest, the soul, being set in motion and awake, administers her own household, and of herself performs all the acts of the body. For the body when asleep has no perception; but the soul when awake has cognizance of all things—sees what is visible, hears what is audible, walks, touches, feels pain, ponders. In a word, all the functions of body and of soul are performed by the soul during sleep. Whoever, therefore, knows how to interpret these acts aright knows a great part of wisdom"* (Loeb, Vol. IV, pp421,423).

Freud could not have put it better.

The unusual significance of haemorrhoids

No age, even the most enlightened, is free from illogical and groundless ideas about health and disease, even in mainstream medicine. In our own times, the almost desperate quest to attribute a physical basis to a series of obviously psychosomatic disorders is probably a good example—an unfortunate trend, which leaves the patients without the treatment they need, sometimes with disastrous consequences.

The subject of haemorrhoids is one where logic deserted the Hippocratic doctors. Here is how they felt that haemorrhoids should be treated:

REGIMEN IN ACUTE DISEASES (APPENDIX), Ch. 62: *"Treat haemorrhoids, too, in the same way: first thrust through a very long thick thread of greasy wool, and then tie them off, for this makes the treatment more effective. Then, after squeezing them out, use a putrefacient; do not wash until the haemorrhoids are fallen off, and always leave one behind"* (Loeb, Vol. VI, p323).

Always leave one haemorrhoid? The explanation is given in several places, including these three quite different treatises:

HUMOURS, Ch. XX: *"Sufferers from haemorrhoids are attacked neither by pleurisy, nor by pneumonia, nor by spreading ulcer, nor by boils, nor by swellings, nor perhaps by skin-eruptions and skin-diseases. However, unseasonably cured, many have been quickly caught by such diseases, and, moreover, in a fatal manner"* (Loeb, Vol. IV, p93).

APHORISMS 6th SECTION, Number XII: *"When a patient has been cured of chronic hemorrhoids, unless one be kept, there is a danger lest dropsy or consumption supervene"* (Loeb, Vol. IV, p183).

EPIDEMICS IV, Ch. 58: *"Alcippus had hemorrhoids, was prevented from being treated. When he was treated he went mad"* (Loeb, Vol. VII, p151).

Alcippus clearly should have listened to his doctors and not had all his haemorrhoids treated!

Miscellaneous misconceptions

The Corpus has a large number of other fanciful propositions, put forward as sober fact. Here are a few examples, among many possible:

Breast size and spontaneous abortion
APHORISMS 5th SECTION, Number XXXVIII: *"When a woman is pregnant with twins, should either breast become thin, she loses one child. If the right breast become thin, she loses the male child; if the left, the female"* (Loeb, Vol. IV, p167).

Baldness and varicose veins
APHORISMS 6th SECTION, Number XXXIV: *"Bald people are not subject to varicose veins; bald people who get varicose veins grow hair again"* (Vol. IV, p187).

Nutrition of the fetus in utero
In the case of the following statement, about how a foetus obtains nutrition, it is easy to see the erroneous line of thought. The

unjustified assumption is that the presence of faecal material in the intestines indicates that food must have been taken orally. On this false assumption, the author of Fleshes built a rather fanciful theory (including the fanning of a woman's body heat by her breath), presented here as fact:

FLESHES, Ch. 6: *"For example the fetus in the belly continually sucks with its lips from the uterus of the mother and draws nourishment and breath to its heart inside, for this breath is hottest in the fetus just at the time that the mother is inspiring. To this (the fetus's heart) and to the rest of the body, too, heat gives movement, and to all other things. If anyone asks you how you know that the fetus draws and sucks in the uterus, you may reply as follows. Both humans and animals have faeces in their intestines at the time of birth, and immediately at birth pass stools—but there would be no faeces, if the fetus did not suck in the uterus. Nor would a baby know how to suck from the breast immediately at birth, if it did not also suck in the uterus"* (Loeb, Vol. VIII, p143).

Some interesting concepts

There are a great many things I could have put in this section, but here are those I found of most interest.

Epilepsy and the seat of consciousness
The author of The Sacred Disease correctly attributed consciousness to the brain, and considered epilepsy to be related in some way to brain function. He puts it very beautifully thus:

THE SACRED DISEASE, Ch. XVII: *"Men ought to know that from the brain, and from the brain only, arise our pleasures, joys, laughter and jests, as well as our sorrows, pains, griefs and tears. Through it, in particular, we think, see, hear, and distinguish the ugly from the beautiful, the bad from the good, the pleasant from the unpleasant"* (Loeb, Vol. II, p175).

THE SACRED DISEASE, Ch. VI: *"The fact is that the cause of this affection, as of the more serious diseases generally, is the brain. The manner and the cause I will now set forth clearly"* (Loeb, Vol. II, p153).

Ice packs for joint pains
A few years ago, while lying down for inordinate lengths of time with ice packs on an injured knee, I remember asking the physiotherapist if there had been any controlled trials for this treatment. She replied that she had no time for such trials, which I took a bit disdainfully. I might have been a little less supercilious had I known that her treatment has a very long and honourable history:

APHORISMS, Section V, Ch. XXV: *"Swellings and pains in the joints, without sores, whether from gout or from sprains, in most cases are relieved by a copious affusion of cold water, which reduces the swelling and removes the pain"* (Loeb, Vol. IV, p165).

The origin of pus

Overheated blood was considered the source of pus:

ULCERS, Ch. 1: *"A lesion becomes purulent when chills and throbbing occur, for lesions become inflamed when they are about to suppurate, and they suppurate when the blood in them is altered and heated until it putrefies and becomes pus"* (Loeb, Vol. VIII, p345).

Oedema

The appearance of fluid in the tissues was ascribed to the overheating and melting of fat:

INTERNAL AFFECTIONS, Ch. 22: *"From phlegm the most frequent change is to dropsy: fat melts, from the burning heat of the phlegm, and becomes water"* (Loeb, Vol. VI, p145).

The 'treatment' of oedema, mentioned on a couple of occasions in the Corpus, consisted of multiple skin incisions, which probably did more harm than good:

PLACES IN MAN, Ch. 25: *"In a child you must treat dropsy as follows. Open the areas that are swollen and full of water by making numerous small incisions with a scalpel; make these openings in every part of the body. Administer vapour-baths, and anoint all the openings with a warming medication"* (Loeb, Vol. VIII, p65).

Possible antimicrobial agents

The use of wine to irrigate the space left after draining an empyema was previously considered as possibly contributing to the control of infection. Wine is also used in the following piece, to wash wounds. Perhaps, more importantly, a mixture of substances including copper is applied to wounds with the specific purpose of preventing suppuration. Copper is known to suppress microbial growth. Here is the potion:

ULCERS, Ch. 13: *"Dry things prevent new wounds from suppurating; apply them either after washing the wound off with vinegar or sponging it off with wine. Dust on fine lead powder triturated with copper oxide; also sprinkle on shavings of nettle-tree wood, also copper scales, also alum, also copper ore (chalcitis) together with copper, also copper ore alone or together with the shavings of nettle-tree wood"* (Loeb, Vol. VIII, p359).

Tourniquet pressure and venesection
It is very interesting to note that the author of Epidemics II was aware that a low pressure tourniquet (above venous but below arterial pressure) increased blood flow at venesection, whereas a tight tourniquet (above arterial pressure) stopped blood flow:
> EPIDEMICS II, Section 3, Ch. 14: *"You should know, too, the bindings send the blood forth in phlebotomy, but tight ones hold it back"* (Loeb, Vol. VII, p61).

There was a clue here, for the conceptual leap to the discovery of the circulation of the blood. However, it went unnoticed and that discovery had to wait another 2,000 years or so for William Harvey (1578–1657).

The most famous aphorism
There are 412 aphorisms in all, arranged since ancient times into seven sections. The most famous is the first, the opening lines of which are well known, and give a broad philosophical view on medical practice:
> APHORISMS, SECTION 1, Number 1: *"Life is short, the Art long, opportunity fleeting, experiment treacherous, judgement difficult"* (Loeb, Vol. IV, p99).

Obscurity in the Corpus

The passage of over 2,000 years has removed the language of the Hippocratic doctor from the context that gave it precise meaning. However, some parts of the Corpus (fortunately few) are almost mystic in their style, as in the opening chapter of Humours:
> HUMOURS, Ch. I: *"The colours of the humours, where there is no ebb of them, is like that of flowers. They must be drawn along the suitable parts whither they tend, except those whose coction comes in due time. Coction tends outwards or inwards, or in any other necessary direction. Caution. Lack of experience. Difficulty of learning by experience. Falling out of hair. Emptiness of bowels, for the lower, repletion, for the upper, nourishment. Tendency upwards; tendency downwards. Spontaneous movements upwards, downwards; beneficial, harmful. Congenital constitution, country, habit, age, season, constitution of the disease, excess, defect, the deficient and the amount of the deficiency, or the contrary"* (Loeb, Vol. IV, pp63,65).

WHS Jones, the translator of Volume IV, suggested that the obscurity in these cases might have been intentional, perhaps having a coded meaning for those initiated into the 'brotherhood'. We shall probably never know.

Chapter 10

Ancient clinical genetics

One of the things we take for granted, but which could inspire wonder in the ancients, is the transmission of parental characteristics to children. In the case of the mother, the fact that the baby grows in her body and is derived from her body provided an explanation of sorts. But how could a father transmit his characteristics (e.g. red hair, tallness, a large nose) to his children by way only of a small volume of amorphous ejaculate?

Apart from the treatise On Generation, which deals specifically with this issue, there are two main references to inheritance in the other treatises. Both take the view, popularized in modern times by Jean Baptiste Lamarck (1744–1829) and referred to as Lamarckism, that acquired characteristics can be passed on to one's children. The author of Airs Waters Places describes a tribe known as Longheads, who originally induced long-headedness by forceful bandaging of children's heads, but who subsequently produced long-headedness without bandaging:

> AIRS WATERS PLACES, Ch. XIV: *"I will begin with the Longheads. There is no other race at all with heads like theirs. Originally custom was chiefly responsible for the length of the head, but now custom is reinforced by nature. Those that have the longest heads they consider the noblest, and their custom is as follows. As soon as a child is born they remodel its head with their hands, while it is still soft and the body tender, and force it to increase in length by applying bandages and suitable appliances, which spoil the roundness of the head and increase its length. Custom originally so acted that through force such a nature came into being; but as time went on the process became natural, so that custom no longer exercised compulsion. For the seed comes from all parts of the body, healthy seed from healthy parts, diseased seed from diseased parts. If, therefore, bald parents have for the most part bald children, grey-eyed parents grey-eyed children, squinting parents squinting children, and so on with other physical peculiarities, what prevents a long-headed parent having a long-headed child?"* (Loeb, Vol. I, p111).

The essential concept was that the seed came from all parts of the body, and reflected the part from which it came. This same concept is applied to the inheritance of disease. The author of The Sacred Disease thought that epilepsy had a hereditary origin. Note the

69

interesting and very striking similarity in the wording of this
quotation to the preceding quotation (the basis for the similarity is
unknown):

THE SACRED DISEASE, Ch. V: *Its origin, like that of other
diseases, lies in heredity. For if a phlegmatic parent has a
phlegmatic child, a bilious parent a bilious child, a consumptive
parent a consumptive child, and a splenetic parent a splenetic
child, there is nothing to prevent some of the children suffering
from this disease when one or the other of the parents suffered
from it; for the seed comes from every part of the body, healthy
seed from the healthy parts, diseased seed from the diseased
parts"* (Loeb, Vol. II, p151).

The treatise On Generation gives essentially the same principles as
those just cited: that semen is derived from all parts of the body, in
both males and females. With this hypothesis, the inheritance of
paternal red hair, or parental disease, makes some sort of sense.

Aristotle, whose father apparently was a doctor, would have been
aware of Hippocratic ideas on reproduction. The Hippocratic
treatises had probably all been written by the time he started his
work (although they were not collated into the Corpus during
his lifetime). Interestingly, Aristotle was uncompromising in his
derision of Hippocratic views on reproduction:

ARISTOTLE. GENERATION OF ANIMALS. BOOK I, Ch.
XVIII: *"As it is, they talk as though even the shoes which the
parent wears were included among the sources from which the
semen is drawn, for on the whole a son who resembles his father
wears shoes that resemble his"* (Loeb, p69).

ARISTOTLE. GENERATION OF ANIMALS. BOOK I, Ch.
XVIII: *"And as for asserting that some of the semen is sinew and
bone—well, the statement is quite over our heads"* (Loeb, p65).

ARISTOTLE. GENERATION OF ANIMALS. BOOK I, Ch.
XVIII: *"As for mutilated offspring being produced by mutilated
parents, the cause is the same as that which makes offspring
resemble their parents. And anyway, not all offspring of
mutilated parents are mutilated, any more than all offspring
resemble their parents. The cause of these things we must
consider later; the problem in both cases is the same"* (Loeb, p71).

The high quality of the scientific questions asked by Aristotle is well
illustrated in the following piece:

ARISTOTLE. GENERATION OF ANIMALS. BOOK I: *"By this
means we shall be able to give a clear answer to the following
questions: Does the female discharge semen as the male does,
which would mean that the object formed is a single mixture*

*produced from two semens; or is there no discharge of semen from
the female? And if there is none, then does the female contribute
nothing whatever to generation, merely providing a place where
generation may happen; or does it contribute something else, and
if so, how and in what manner does it do so?"* (Loeb, p89).

He discusses the nature of male and female semen, and gives what I
think is a remarkably prescient and intuitive definition of DNA, long
before it was ever dreamt of:

ARISTOTLE. GENERATION OF ANIMALS. BOOK I: *"Thus,
the semen of the hand or of the face or the whole animal really is
hand or face or a whole animal though in an undifferentiated way;
in other words, what each of those is* in actuality, *such the semen is*
potentially, *whether in respect of its own proper bulk, or because it
has some* dynamis *within itself"* (Loeb, p91).

The next 2,500 years

I think it is an interesting characteristic of human nature to believe that, although there might be obvious gaps in our knowledge of the world, we in fact understand things reasonably well. We create hypotheses to give ourselves this comfortable feeling. However, who can doubt that monumental discoveries in biology, medicine and the physical sciences are waiting to be made in the coming centuries and millennia? Is it not very likely that we shall seem as desperately ignorant to those future, knowing generations as the Hippocratic doctors now seem to us? In spite of this, I think you will agree that our general attitude is similar to that of the Hippocratic doctors, and that this at least will not change with the passage of time:

PLACES IN MAN: Ch. 46: *"Medicine in its present state is, it seems to me, by now completely discovered, insofar as it teaches in each instance the particular details and the correct measures. For anyone who has an understanding of medicine in this way depends very little upon good luck, but is able to do good with or without luck. For the whole of medicine has been established, and the excellent principles discovered in it clearly have very little need of good luck"* (Loeb, Vol. VIII, p93).

References

1. Jones WHS. *Hippocrates, Volume I.* London: Loeb Classical Library, Harvard University Press, 1923.
2. Jones WHS. *Hippocrates, Volume II.* London: Loeb Classical Library, Harvard University Press, 1923.
3. Withington ET. *Hippocrates, Volume III.* London: Loeb Classical Library, Harvard University Press, 1928.
4. Jones WHS. *Hippocrates, Volume IV.* London: Loeb Classical Library, Harvard University Press, 1931.
5. Potter P. *Hippocrates, Volume V.* London: Loeb Classical Library, Harvard University Press, 1988.
6. Potter P. *Hippocrates, Volume VI.* London: Loeb Classical Library, Harvard University Press, 1988.
7. Smith WD. *Hippocrates, Volume VII.* London: Loeb Classical Library, Harvard University Press, 1994.
8. Potter P. *Hippocrates, Volume VIII.* London: Loeb Classical Library, Harvard University Press, 1995.
9. Lonie IM. *The seed in: Hippocratic writings.* Lloyd GER, ed. London: Penguin Classics, 1978.
10. Peck AL. *Aristotle. Generation of animals.* London: Loeb Classical Library, Harvard University Press, 1942.
11. Conrad LI, Neve M, Nutton V, Porter R, Wear A. *The Western medical tradition, 800BC–1800AD.* Cambridge: Cambridge University Press, 1995.
12. Meador CK. The last well person. *N Engl J Med* 1994; **330**: 440–41.

Glossary of medical terms

Acetabulum
Cup-shaped structure on pelvic bone into which the rounded head of the femur fits, to make the hip joint.

Analgesia
Relief of pain.

Cautery
Burning of skin or tissues, usually by the application of a very hot metal instrument.

Clyster
An infusion of fluid into the rectum and colon.

Compound fracture
A fracture where the ends of the broken bone protrude through the skin.

Cyanotic
Blue colour because of inadequate oxygenation of the blood.

DNA
Deoxyribonucleic acid, the chemical substance of which genes and chromosomes are made.

Dropsy
A lay term for oedema.

Dura mater
The tough membrane covering the brain.

Effusion
An abnormal accumulation of fluid in a body cavity.

Emetic
A substance which induces vomiting.

Empyema
Pus in the pleural cavity, i.e. the space in the chest between the lung and the chest wall (normally a potential space only).

Enemas
Medications inserted into the rectum, frequently to induce defecation.

Eschar
A layer of dry, dead tissue caused by burning or other means.

Femur
Thigh bone.

Fibula
Thin bone of lower leg, on the outer side of the tibia.

Homeostasis
The maintenance of a constant level.

Meconium
The contents of the intestine of the foetus or new-born baby.

Micturition
The passing of urine.

Oedema
Excess fluid in the tissues.

Opisthotonus
Arching of back consequent on muscle spasm.

Phlegm
Mucous secretion.

Ptyalism
Excessive salivation.

Puerperal
Around the time of birth.

Purulent
Containing pus.

Reduction of dislocations
Putting the dislocated bones back into joint.

Reduction of fractures
Re-aligning the broken bones.

Regimen
Diet and exercise.

Rigor
Intense shivering and shaking preceding a fever.

Suppuration
The production of pus.

Thalassaemia
A genetic disorder of the haemoglobin (oxygen carrying) protein of red blood cells.

Tibia
Main bone of the lower leg.

Trephine
To make a hole in the skull bone.

Uvula
The small, midline projection from the soft palate at the back of the roof of the mouth.

Vasoconstriction
Constriction of blood vessels, reducing flow.

Vasodilation
Dilation of blood vessels, increasing flow.

Venesection
Drawing blood from veins.

About the author

Professor John Fabre graduated in medicine in 1968, and following House Officer posts at the Royal Melbourne Hospital, obtained his PhD from the University of Melbourne in 1973. He then came to England on a 3 year Royal Society Research Fellowship and has pursued his subsequent career in England. He was a Wellcome Senior Clinical Research Fellow in Oxford from 1975, and a Research Professor of the Royal College of Surgeons in East Grinstead, Sussex from 1982. In 1991, he moved to the Institute of Child Health, University College London Medical School, London, as the British Heart Foundation Professor of Paediatric Cardiology and Head of the Division of Cell and Molecular Biology. His wife, also a doctor, is in General Practice in East Sussex.